CASH & CREDIT
Accounting

workbook

NVQ LEVEL 2
ACCOUNTING

David Cox
Michael Fardon

OSBORNE
BOOKS

Published by Osborne Books Limited
Unit 1B Everoak Estate
Bromyard Road
Worcester
WR2 5HN
Tel 01905 748071

Printed by the Bath Press, Bath.

British Library Cataloguing in Publication Data
A catalogue record for this book is available from the British Library

ISBN 1 872962 08 4

CONTENTS

central assessment processing exercises and short questions

central assessment communication tasks

appendix – photocopiable documents

ACKNOWLEDGEMENTS

The authors wish to thank the following for their help with the compilation, reading and production of this workbook: Jean Cox, Michael Gilbert, Rosemary Griffiths, Roger Petheram and Marjorie Pierce.

Particular thanks are due to the Association of Accounting Technicians for their generous permission for the reproduction of tasks from sample Devolved Assessments and from past Central Assessments.

HOW TO USE THIS BOOK

Cash & Credit Accounting Workbook is designed to be used alongside Osborne Books' *Cash & Credit Accounting Tutorial* and is ideal for student use in the classroom, at home and on distance learning courses.

Cash & Credit Accounting Workbook is divided into three separate sections: Workbook Activities, Devolved Assessment tasks and Central Assessment tasks.

The Devolved and Central Assessment tasks in this workbook provide, within the text, the documents and accounts that need to be completed. In the case of the Workbook Activities, most documents are provided in the text, but some formats, eg double-entry accounts, journals, cash books, are not. They are reproduced in the Appendix at the end of the book, and may be photocopied.

workbook activities

Workbook activities are self-contained exercises which are designed to be used to supplement the activities in the tutorial text. Many of them are more extended than the exercises in *Cash & Credit Accounting Tutorial* and provide useful practice for students preparing for Assessments.

Devolved Assessments tasks

There is a set of tasks for each of the NCVQ units. 'Davies Cash & Carry' provides practice in the Cash Accounting unit while 'Hornet Stationery' is based on the Credit Accounting unit. At the beginning of each set of tasks is a table which sets out the performance criteria covered by individual tasks.

Central Assessment tasks

This section comprises tasks taken from AAT past Central Assessments. In each case the processing exercise is followed by the short question section, the two being closely inter-related. The communication exercises are set in a section of their own, cross-referenced to the appropriate processing exercise.

answers

Answers are not provided in the text. A Tutor Pack is available separately. Please telephone Osborne Books on 01905 748071 for details.

David Cox
Michael Fardon

Summer 1997

TUTOR HINTS –
PREPARING FOR ASSESSMENTS

The following hints have been provided by an experienced AAT tutor and are designed to help students prepare for AAT assessments.

Devolved Assessments

1   Ensure that you have covered all the topics covered by the specifications – this means reading your tutorial text and then practising all aspects of the work involved.

2   Attempt all the tasks set in a Devolved Assessment.

3   You must have a sound understanding of
   • invoices, credit notes and associated documents
   • the principles of Value Added Tax
   • the double-entry system
   • bank reconciliation statements
   • balancing the control account with the total of the ledger accounts

4   You must be able to analyse transactions, for example in a daybook over a range of products.

5   Always ensure that you:
   • check important details
   • understand the relationship between cash discounts and the calculation of VAT
   • understand that VAT is set out in the daybooks for credit transactions and in the cash book for cash transactions

6   Appreciate that there are different ways of setting out the same type of account, eg cash books with a variety of analysis columns

Central Assessments – the format

There are three sections in a Central Assessment: the processing exercise, short-answer questions and a communication exercise. You must answer all three sections and achieve a level of competence in each.

The *Processing Exercise* normally involves posting opening balances, processing transactions and then balancing accounts. You must have a good understanding of the double-entry system. It is essential that you know how cash books and control accounts fit into the ledger system.

Twenty *short questions* are asked in a variety of styles and often relate to the processing exercise which they follow. They cover accounting principles, data processing and legal issues. You should ensure that you have a thorough understanding of the underpinning knowledge which is covered in your tutorial text. Legal issues are covered specifically in Osborne Books' *Cash & Credit Accounting Tutorial,* Chapter 19, which contains examples of short questions relating to legal problems.

The final section of the Central Assessment is the *Communication Exercise.* The memorandum and letter format is used as a means of testing understanding of the underpinning knowledge of accounting principles. You must be familiar with the correct format of these documents. They are covered in Osborne Books' *Cash & Credit Accounting Tutorial,* Chapter 18, which contains examples of formats and letter texts.

Central Assessments – 10 additional hints

1   If you have never been to the centre where you are doing the assessment, make sure that you know where it is. If possible, do not work late the evening before an assessment. Instead, check you have everything ready including calculator (and battery) and pens.

2   Arrive in plenty of time for the assessment.

3   At the start ensure that you have the correct assessment in front of you. Listen to the instructions read to you by the supervisor.

4   When you start, do not rush. Read through carefully, check the time allowed. Plan out your time.

5.   If you are stuck, read the task again; think for a few minutes before moving on.

6   Do not worry about what other people are doing. Concentrate on completing your assessment.

7   Make sure that you have completed each task as requested.

8   When you have finished, check that you have completed everything and look again at anything you are not sure about.

9   Check your calculations.

10   Do not change anything that you have already written until you are completely sure that you originally made an error. The first answer is very often the right answer.

Section 1

workbook activities

This section contains activities which are suitable for use with the individual chapters of 'Cash & Credit Accounting Tutorial' from Osborne Books.

1 INTRODUCTION TO ACCOUNTING

NVQ coverage

knowledge and understanding

- accounting systems of organisations
- the main types of account

WORKBOOK ACTIVITIES

1.1 What is the difference between a sole trader, a partnership and a limited company in terms of the following factors?

- ownership of the business
- the ability to specialise in one area of the business
- liability for business debts
- the need to keep accounting records

Set out your answer in the form of a table with the above factors as headings.

1.2 Write down in the form of short numbered sentences the advantages and disadvantages of a basic computer accounting system when compared with a manual system.

1.3 The accounting records of Tom's sole trader business show the following account totals at the end of the year:

Capital (money invested by the owner)	£185,000
Business premises	£100,000
Bank overdraft (owed to the bank)	£80,000
Computers used in the business	£50,000
Stock held by the business	£75,000
Creditors (amounts owed by the business)	£20,000
Debtors (money owed to the business)	£60,000

(a) Sort the above accounts under the three categories set out below, and total each category:
- assets
- liabilities
- capital

(b) Insert the three totals into the accounting equation

assets   minus   liabilities   equals   capital

If the equation does not balance, check your categories in (a) above.

(c) Tom has increased the bank overdraft to buy more stock costing £10,000. Adjust the totals in the equation. It should still balance; if it does not, check your workings.

NVQ coverage

unit 2 element 1

- *process documents relating to goods and services supplied on credit*

2 DOCUMENTS - SELLING ON CREDIT

INTRODUCTION

You work as an accounts assistant at Compusupply Limited, a business which sells computer supplies such as disks and listing paper to a wide range of customers.

It is your job to process incoming orders which arrive in the form of purchase orders, faxes and telephoned orders.

You also deal with the accounting side of returned goods and you issue credit notes when credit is due.

You are also in charge of sending out statements.

You are authorised to issue invoices without reference to the acounts supervisor as long as the account is kept within its credit limit. You are required to refer any difficulties and likely excesses over credit limits to your supervisor.

Compusupply Limited normally operates a computer accounting system, but unfortunately the system has crashed and you have been asked to process all the necessary documents by hand until the hard disk has been repaired. The crash is a serious one, so you may be without the computer for over a week.

You have been given the following information:

CUSTOMER DETAILS
(EXTRACTS FROM COMPUSUPPLY FILES)

customer	account number	discount %	credit limit £	balance £
Andrews R C	234	10	1000	750.00
Harber Employment Agency	341	10	1000	456.75
Case, Justin	209	10	1000	218.50
P C Mack Limited	197	20	5000	3190.00
Singh, I	222	10	1000	00.00
Singh, R, Retail	265	20	3500	2185.00
Townsend Litho	409	20	5000	4756.75
Zebra Designs Ltd	376	10	1000	487.50

COMPUSUPPLY CATALOGUE (EXTRACT)

code	product	unit price	£ (excl VAT)
OMHD10	OM 3.5 inch diskettes DSHD	boxes of 10	5.50
Z100	Zip 100MB cartridges	each	12.99
LP80	Computer listing paper 80 column	2000 sheet box	14.99
LP132	Computer listing paper 132 column	2000 sheet box	19.99
SQ44	Syquest disk 44MB	each	36.99
SQ88	Syquest disk 88MB	each	42.99
SQ200	Syquest disk 200MB	each	49.99
DB40	Floppy storage box (40 disks)	each	4.99
DB80	Floppy storage box (80 disks)	each	5.99
AG1	VDU anti-glare screen (mesh)	each	11.99
AG2	VDU anti-glare screen (glass)	each	19.99

ACTIVITIES

2.1 You have to check a batch of invoices to make sure the correct customer trade discount of 10% has been applied.

The totals before deduction of discount are:

(a)   £67.50

(b)   £45.00

(c)   £107.95

(d)   £12,567.95

(e)   £12.75

(f)   £89.00

(g)   £400.00

(h)   £17,450.50

(i)   £1.75

(j)   £30.33

You are to work out the net totals before VAT. Remember to round up or down to nearest penny.

2.2   You have to check the VAT calculation on a further batch of invoices. The totals before VAT are:

(a)   £40.00

(b)   £8.00

(c)   £75.00

(d)   £675.50

You are to work out the VAT *and* the final total in each case. Remember to round VAT amounts down to the nearest penny in each case.

2.3   Your colleague reminds you that a cash discount of 2.5% is due on the four invoices in the previous task. You are to adjust the VAT to allow for a cash discount of 2.5% and recalculate the totals, but remembering that the net total shown on the invoice will *not* be reduced - only the VAT amount.

2.4   In the morning post there are three purchase orders. You are to complete invoices for all three orders. The date is 20 October 1997 and the invoices should be numbered consecutively from 309530. Blank invoices are printed on the pages that follow the purchase orders.

JUSTIN CASE *insurance services*	PURCHASE ORDER
2 Oakfield Business Centre Letchfield LT1 7TR Tel 01903 273423	

TO

Compusupply Limited Unit 17 Elgar Estate, Broadfield, BR7 4ER	purchase order no 58345 date 17 October 1997

product code	quantity	description
LP80	2 boxes	Computer listing paper, 80 columns

Authorised   signature......*J Case*..date...................*17.10.97*...............

R SINGH RETAIL

2 The Crescent
Broadfield
BR6 3TR
Tel 01908 456291

PURCHASE ORDER

TO

Compusupply Limited
Unit 17 Elgar Estate,
Broadfield, BR7 4ER

purchase order no   353453

date   17 October 1997

product code	quantity	description
OMHD10	10	OM 3.5 inch floppy disks

Authorised   signature..... *R Singh* ....date................ *17.10.97* ....

P C Mack Ltd

57 New Road
Broadfield
BR3 6TF
Tel 01908 456291

PURCHASE ORDER

TO

Compusupply Limited
Unit 17 Elgar Estate,
Broadfield, BR7 4ER

purchase order no 14535

date   15 October 1997

product code	quantity	description
SQ44	2	Syquest 44MB disks

Authorised   signature..... *Steve Gates* ....date.... *15.10.97* ......

INVOICE
COMPUSUPPLY LIMITED

Unit 17 Elgar Estate, Broadfield, BR7 4ER
Tel 01908 765756 Fax 01908 765777 Email rob@compusupply.u-net.com
VAT Reg GB 0745 4689 13

invoice to

Justin Case insurance services
2 Oakfield Business Centre
Letchfield
LT1 7TR

invoice no 309530

account 209

your reference 58345

date/tax point 20 October 1997

product code	description	quantity	price	unit	total	discount %	net
LP80	Computer listing Paper, 80 columns	2 boxes	14.99	box (2000)	29.98	3.00	26.98
					goods total		26.98

terms
Net monthly
Carriage paid
E & OE

VAT	4.72
TOTAL	31.70

INVOICE
COMPUSUPPLY LIMITED

Unit 17 Elgar Estate, Broadfield, BR7 4ER
Tel 01908 765756 Fax 01908 765777 Email rob@compusupply.u-net.com
VAT Reg GB 0745 4689 13

invoice to

R. Singh Retail
2 The Crescent
Broadfield
BR6 3TR

invoice no 309531

account 265

your reference 353453

date/tax point 20 October 1997

product code	description	quantity	price	unit	total	discount %	net
OMHDID om	3.5 inch floppy disks	10	5.50	box (10)	5.50	1.10	4.40
					goods total		4.40

terms
Net monthly
Carriage paid
E & OE

Qty Sold 10

VAT	.77
TOTAL	5.17

INVOICE
COMPUSUPPLY LIMITED
Unit 17 Elgar Estate, Broadfield, BR7 4ER
Tel 01908 765756 Fax 01908 765777 Email rob@compusupply.u-net.com
VAT Reg GB 0745 4689 13

invoice to

P C Mack Ltd
57 New Road
Broadfield
BR3 6TF

invoice no   309532

account   197

your reference   14535

date/tax point   20 October 1997

product code	description	quantity	price	unit	total	discount %	net
SQ44	Syquest 44MB disks	2	36.99	each	73.98	14.80	59.18

goods total	59.18
VAT	10.35
TOTAL	69.53

terms
Net monthly
Carriage paid
E & OE

2.5   Check the invoice extracts shown below with the Catalogue and customer discount list, making sure that the details and the calculations are correct. Where there are errors, correct them in red ink.

Note: VAT is always rounded down to the nearest penny. No cash discounts are involved.

(a)   Invoice to R C Andrews

code	description	quantity	price	total	discount %	net
AG1 AG2	VDU anti-glare screen (glass)	1	19.99	19.99	20 10	15.99 17.99

goods total	15.99 17.99
VAT @ 17.5%	2.79 3.14
TOTAL	18.78 21.13

(b) Invoice to I Singh

code	description	quantity	price	total	discount %	net
DB40	Floppy storage box (40)	4	4.99	19.96	10	15.97 _17.96_

goods total	15.97 _17.96_
VAT @ 17.5%	2.79 _3.14_
TOTAL	13.18 _21.10_

(c) Invoice to Harber Employment Agency

code	description	quantity	price	total	discount %	net
OMHD10	OM 3.5 inch disks DSHD	10 boxes	5.50	55.00	20 _10_	44.00 _49.50_

goods total	44.00 _49.50_
VAT @ 17.5%	7.70 _8.66_
TOTAL	51.70 _58.16_

2.6   When you return from lunch there are two telephone messages for you:

> # telephone message
>
> **to**   *order processing*
>
> **date**   *20.10.97*   **time**   *13.45*
>
> *Townsend Litho telephoned. They want to order ten 200MB Syquest disks as soon as possible. Can you get them off by carrier today? Thanks. Sue.*

Townsend Litho is a well-established customer with a good record of paying on time.

> # telephone message
>
> **to**   *order processing*
>
> **date**   *20.10.97*   **time**   *13.45*
>
> *Zebra Designs called. They want a box of computer listing paper. 80 columns.*
>
> *Thanks. Hanif.*

On your return from lunch a colleague mentions that he thought he saw a notice in the local paper about Zebra Designs going 'bust'. You look in the official announcement column of the paper and see that your colleague is correct – a creditors' meeting is called for next Monday. Zebra Designs is in deep financial trouble.

You are to

(a)   State what you would do in response to the two telephone messages.

(b)   State the likely outcome of the two situations.

2.7   It is now a week later – 27 October 1997 – and the computer system is still not working, so you have to complete all documents by hand.

During the course of the day you receive two returns notes (printed on the next page)

You are to

(a)   Write down on the R Singh Retail returns note what has gone wrong with the order.

(b)   Complete the credit notes as requested (the documents are printed on the page following the returns notes).

R SINGH RETAIL

2 The Crescent
Broadfield
BR6 3TR
Tel 01908 456291

RETURNS NOTE

10 Boxes have been sent by mistake when only one box should have been sent. (10 disks).

TO

Compusupply Limited
Unit 17 Elgar Estate,
Broadfield, BR7 4ER

returns note no	353453
date	22 October 1997

product code	quantity	description
OMHD10	9 boxes	OM 3.5 inch floppy disks

REASON FOR RETURN: too many disks sent – only 10 disks ordered. Please credit.

signature......*R Singh*......date......*22.10.97*......

P C Mack Ltd

57 New Road
Broadfield
BR3 6TF
Tel 01908 456291

RETURNS NOTE

TO

Compusupply Limited
Unit 17 Elgar Estate,
Broadfield, BR7 4ER

purchase order no	14535
date	23 October 1997

product code	quantity	description
SQ44	1	Syquest 44MB data disk.

REASON FOR RETURN: faulty disk. Please credit.

signature......*Steve Gates*......date......*23.10.97*......

━━━━━━ **CREDIT NOTE** ━━━━━━

COMPUSUPPLY LIMITED

Unit 17 Elgar Estate, Broadfield, BR7 4ER
Tel 01908 765756 Fax 01908 765777 Email rob@compusupply.u-net.com
VAT Reg GB 0745 4689 13

to

R. Singh Retail
2 The Crescent
Broadfield
BR6 3TR

credit note no   1
account   265
your reference 353453
our invoice   309531
date/tax point 27 October 1977

product code	description	quantity	price	unit	total	discount %	net
OMHDIO	OM 3.5 inch Floppy disks	9 boxes	5.50	box (10)	49.50	9.90	39.60

goods total	39.60
VAT	6.93
TOTAL	46.53

REASON FOR CREDIT: Too many disks sent - only 10 disks ordered, not 10 boxes.

━━━━━━ **CREDIT NOTE** ━━━━━━

COMPUSUPPLY LIMITED

Unit 17 Elgar Estate, Broadfield, BR7 4ER
Tel 01908 765756 Fax 01908 765777 Email rob@compusupply.u-net.com
VAT Reg GB 0745 4689 13

to

P C Mack Ltd
57 New Road
Broadfield
BR3 6TF

credit note no   2
account   197
your reference 14535
our invoice   309532
date/tax point 27 October 1997

product code	description	quantity	price	unit	total	discount %	net
SQ44	Syquest 44MB data disk	1	36.99	each	36.99	7.40	29.59

goods total	29.59
VAT	5.17
TOTAL	34.76

REASON FOR CREDIT: Faulty disk

2.8 It is now 31 October. The computer accounts package has been fixed and will start operating again from Monday 3 November. In the meantime you have to make out the customer statements. Using the start-of-month balances and all the transactions during the month, complete statements for R Singh Retail, P C Mack Limited and Justin Case. The statements are printed in the text.

The two payments you have received for these customers is a cheque for £218.50 from Justin Case on October 7 and a cheque for £3190.00 from P C Mack Limited on October 10.

STATEMENT

COMPUSUPPLY LIMITED

Unit 17 Elgar Estate, Broadfield, BR7 4ER
Tel 01908 765756 Fax 01908 765777 Email rob@compusupply.u-net.com
VAT Reg GB 0745 4689 13

to

R. Singh Retail
2 The Crescent
Broadfield
BR6 3TR

account 265

date 31 October 1997

date	details	debit £	credit £	balance £
1997				
1 Oct	Balance B/D	2185.00		2185.00 Dr.
20 Oct	Invoice No. 309531	5.17		2190.17 Dr.
27 Oct	Credit Note CN1		46.53	2143.64 Dr.

AMOUNT NOW DUE	2143.64

— STATEMENT —

COMPUSUPPLY LIMITED

Unit 17 Elgar Estate, Broadfield, BR7 4ER
Tel 01908 765756 Fax 01908 765777 Email rob@compusupply.u-net.com
VAT Reg GB 0745 4689 13

to

P C Mack Ltd
57 New Road
Broadfield
BR3 6TF

account   197

date   31 October 1997

date	details	debit £	credit £	balance £
1997				
1 Oct	Balance B/D	3190.00		3190.00 Dr
20 Oct	Invoice No 309532	69.53		3259.53 Dr
27 Oct	Credit Note CN2		34.76	3224.77 Dr

Recd. a cheque for
£3190 (10th Oct)

AMOUNT NOW DUE	3224.77

STATEMENT

COMPUSUPPLY LIMITED

Unit 17 Elgar Estate, Broadfield, BR7 4ER
Tel 01908 765756 Fax 01908 765777 Email rob@compusupply.u-net.com
VAT Reg GB 0745 4689 13

to

Justin Case Insurance Services
2 Oakfield Business Centre
Letchfield
LT1 7TR

account   209

date   31 October 1997

date	details	debit	credit	balance
1977		£	£	£
1 Oct	Balance B/D	218.50		218.50 Dr.
20 Oct	Invoice No. 309530	31.70		250.20 Dr.

Received a cheque
£218.50 (7/10/)

AMOUNT NOW DUE	250.20

3 DOCUMENTS - BUYING ON CREDIT

WORKBOOK ACTIVITIES

3.1 You have just started work as an accounts assistant in the purchasing department of Litho Printers. Your supervisor has asked you to buy 150 reams (a ream is 500 sheets) of standard quality white A4 copy paper. He said "shop around if you can – prices can vary a lot."

You have telephoned four different stationery suppliers for their stationery catalogues and have made enquiries about special offers on copy paper. The best deals seem to be from Saxon Supplies. An extract from their catalogue (which they have faxed through) is shown below.

SAXON SUPPLIES

Unit 12 Hereward Industrial Estate, Warborough, WA3 5TG

Tel 01807 282482 Fax 01807 282412 Email JJ@Saxon.u-net-com.uk

BARGAINS OF THE MONTH!

reference	product	unit	list price (VAT excl)	sale price (VAT excl)
RCA4	A4 Roxo 80gsm copy paper (white only) standard quality	ream	3.49	2.79
REFA4	A4 Roxo 80gsm copy paper (white – extra fine quality)	ream	4.99	3.49
RLA4	A4 Roxo 80gsm laser paper	ream	5.49	4.99
CCA4	Colour 80gsm copy paper Add code to your order ref: R (red) B (blue) Y (yellow)	ream	5.50	4.50
EWDLP	White self-seal DL envelopes (plain)	1000 box	25.00	10.99
EWDLSS	White self-seal DL envelopes (window)	1000 box	35.00	16.99
N1	'Nifty' air bubble mail envelopes 200mm x 300mm	100 box	22.00	18.00
N2	'Nifty' air bubble mail envelopes 235mm x 370mm	100 box	25.00	21.00
FR15	Fax roll 210mm x 15m	roll	2.85	1.50
FR30	Fax roll 216mm x 30m	roll	5.00	3.50

Your supervisor, who has seen the Saxon Supplies prices, says that she also wants to order 50 fax rolls (30m) and 5 boxes of white self-seal DL window envelopes which are used to send out customer statements.

You are to complete the purchase order shown below for the 150 reams of ordinary white copy paper and the extra items requested by the supervisor. You are authorised to sign the order (use your own name). Saxon Supplies has said over the telephone that you can have an initial 15% discount on all orders. The purchase order number is 2892. The date is 8 December 1997.

PURCHASE ORDER

litho printers

Unit 7 Buttermere Estate
Station Road
Broadfield
BR6 3TR
Tel 01908 456291 Fax 01908 456913

to

purchase order no

date

product code	quantity	description

Authorised   signature..date....................................

3.2   Later in the morning you have to check a delivery note for goods just received against the original purchase order (see page 26). Write a letter to the supplier (see page 27) explaining what is wrong with the delivery. Use your own name and the title 'Accounts Assistant'. The date is 8 December 1997.

PURCHASE ORDER

litho printers

Unit 7 Buttermere Estate
Station Road
Broadfield
BR6 3TR
Tel 01908 456291 Fax 01908 456913

to

Eleco Supplies
79 Broadacre
Boreham
BO7 6TG

purchase order no   3601

date   20 November 1997

product code	quantity	description
23477C	5	Typo office chairs, charcoal

Authorised   signature.....*A Morello*..date...........*20.1197*...............

DELIVERY NOTE

eleco supplies

79 Broadacre
Boreham
BO7 6TG
Tel 01208 070111 Fax 01208 070149

to

Litho Printers Limited
Unit 7 Buttermere Estate
Station Road
Broadfield
BR6 3TR

Delivery Note No   39823
Purchase Order no   3601
Date   5 December 1997
Delivery   Lightning Carriers

product code	quantity	description
22477C	5	Executive chairs, charcoal

Received in good condition

signature...........*R Smithers*................................date..........*8.12.97*.............

litho printers

Unit 7 Buttermere Estate, Station Road,
Broadfield BR6 3TR
Tel 01908 456291 Fax 01908 456913
E-mail ben@litho.u-net.com

Litho Printers Limited. Registered office: Unit 7 Buttermere Estate, Station Road, Broadfield BR6 3TR
Registered in England No 3539857. VAT Reg GB 32 73687 78

3.3 After lunch on the same day (8 December 1997) you have to check three incoming invoices against the appropriate goods received notes which have been raised (see pages 28 to 30). They should be checked for accuracy and to make sure that they apply to the goods supplied. You are to make a list of any errors or discrepancies and pass it to your supervisor on the schedule on page 31. Each of the suppliers normally gives 20% trade discount, but no cash discount.

INVOICE

JUMBO STATIONERY

91 HIGH STREET, BROADFIELD, BR7 4ER
Tel 01908 129426 Fax 01908 129919

invoice to

Litho Printers Limited
Unit 7 Buttermere Estate
Station Road
Broadfield BR6 3TR

invoice no	234672
account	2984
your reference	3627
date/tax point	1 December 1997

product code	description	quantity	price	unit	total	discount %	net
JB234	Jetstream Biros, finepoint, black	20	2.25	box	45.00	10	40.50

terms

Net monthly

Carriage paid

E & OE

goods total	40.50
VAT	7.08
TOTAL	47.58

JAVELIN OFICE MACHINES

invoice

Unit 19 Elgar Estate, Broadfield, BR7 4ER
Tel 01908 765101 Fax 01908 765304

invoice to

Litho Printers Limited
Unit 7 Buttermere Estate
Station Road
Broadfield   BR6 3TR

invoice no	10483
account	935
order reference	3629
date/tax point	2 December 1997

product code	description	quantity	price	unit	total	discount %	net
M17C	Multipoint 17" colour monitor	1	499.00	item	499.00	20	399.20

terms

Net monthly

Carriage paid

E & OE

goods total	399.20
VAT	69.86
TOTAL	469.06

EDWARD HUGHES LIMITED

invoice

Unit 3 Bronglais Estate, Pwllmadoc, LL1 4ER
Tel 01708 323242 Fax 01708 323242 VAT Reg GB 5019 46 2

invoice to

Litho Printers Limited Unit 7 Buttermere Estate Station Road Broadfield BR6 3TR	
invoice no	12931
account	9742
your reference	3628
date/tax point	2 December 1997

product code	description	quantity	price	unit	total	discount %	net
3883	Automatic offset crimper	1	8295.00	unit	8295.00	20	6636.00

goods total	6636.00

terms
Net monthly
Carriage paid
E & OE

VAT	1116.30
TOTAL	7752.30

---

litho printers

GOODS RECEIVED NOTE

GRN no.	301
supplier	Jumbo Stationery
date	3 December 1997

order ref.	quantity	description
3627	15 boxes	Jetstream biros (fine point, black)

received by...*R Nixon*..**checked by**....*I Singh*....................

condition of goods   good   15 boxes

damages

shortages 5 boxes

litho printers   GOODS RECEIVED NOTE

GRN no.   303
supplier   Javelin Office Machines
date   4 December 1997

order ref.	quantity	description
3629	1	Multipoint 17 inch colour monitor

received by..........*J Kennedy*...........................checked by...........*I Singh*.................

condition of goods   good √
                            damages
                            shortages

litho printers   GOODS RECEIVED NOTE

GRN no.   302
supplier   Edward Hughes Ltd
date   4 December 1997

order ref.	quantity	description
3628	1	Automatic offset crimper

received by..........*J Kennedy*...........................checked by...........*M Jones*.................

condition of goods   good √
                            damages
                            shortages

date	Order no.	Action to be taken

3.4 Today it is 12 December 1997 and the stationery order from Saxon Supplies (see Task 3.1) has arrived. The goods received note shows that the correct quantity of goods has been received and that there are no wrong goods or damaged items.

You have now been passed the invoice for checking against the original order (produced in Task 3.1). If there are any problems with the invoice, write them down on the memorandum on the next page. Address the memo to your supervisor, James Ridelle. Use your own name. Your title is Accounts Assistant.

INVOICE

SAXON SUPPLIES

Unit 12 Hereward Industrial Estate, Warborough, WA3 5TG

Tel 01807 282482 Fax 01807 282412 Email JJ@Saxon.u-net-com.uk

invoice to

Litho Printers Limited
Unit 7 Buttermere Estate
Station Road
Broadfield BR6 3TR

invoice no	89422
account	230
your reference	2892
date/tax point	10 December 1997

product code	description	quantity	price	unit	total	discount %	net
RCA4	A4 Roxo 80gsm copy paper	150	3.49	ream	523.50	15	444.98
FR30	Fax roll 216mm x 30mm	50	3.50	unit	175.00	15	148.75
EWDLSS	White self-seal window DL envelopes	5	16.99	box	84.95	15	72.21

terms

Net monthly

Carriage paid

E & OE

goods total	665.94
VAT	116.53
TOTAL	782.47

MEMORANDUM

date
to
from
subject

NVQ coverage

unit 2 elements 1 & 2

- *main types of account*
- *double-entry principles*
- *function of primary records*

4 ACCOUNTING RECORDS

4.1 State into which primary accounting record each of the following prime documents will be recorded:

- sales invoices
- purchases invoices
- credit notes issued
- credit notes received

4.2 In which division of the ledger would you find the following accounts?

- (a) P Patel, a customer
- (b) A Armitage, a supplier
- (c) sales returns account
- (d) bank account
- (e) purchases returns account
- (f) VAT account

4.3 Amit Manufacturing Company has sold goods on credit to Wyvern Retail Limited. Explain in note form the principles of recording this transaction in the accounting systems of both the seller and buyer, including the use of coding. Both businesses are registered for Value Added Tax.

5 ACCOUNTING FOR CREDIT SALES AND SALES RETURNS

Note: photocopiable accounts and daybooks are printed in the Appendix (see page 243).

5.1 Which one of the following will be entered in the sales returns day book?

(a)   sales invoice

(b)   purchases invoice

(c)   credit note received

(d)   credit note issued

Answer (a) or (b) or (c) or (d)

> *In the activities which follow, the rate of Value Added Tax is to be calculated at the current rate (17.5% at the time of writing). When calculating VAT amounts, you should ignore fractions of a penny, ie round down to a whole penny.*
>
> *Leave the folio column blank, and do not use account numbers, unless otherwise stated.*

5.2 Pensax Products Limited manufactures plastic goods which are sold direct to shops. During November 1997 the following credit transactions took place:

1997

3 Nov	Sold goods to Dines Stores £265 + VAT, invoice no. 3592
5 Nov	Sold goods to Raven Retailers Limited, £335 + VAT, invoice no. 3593
6 Nov	Sold goods to Meadow Golf Club £175 + VAT, invoice no. 3594
10 Nov	Sold goods to Wyvern Stores £455 + VAT, invoice no. 3595
11 Nov	Sold goods to Dines Stores £290 + VAT, invoice no. 3596
13 Nov	Sold goods to Teme Sports Limited £315 + VAT, invoice no. 3597
17 Nov	Sold goods to Raven Retailers Limited £1,120 + VAT, invoice no. 3598
19 Nov	Sold goods to Teme Sports Limited £825 + VAT, invoice no. 3599
21 Nov	Sold goods to Dines Stores £354 + VAT, invoice no. 3600
24 Nov	Sold goods to Meadow Golf Club £248 + VAT, invoice no. 3601
27 Nov	Sold goods to Wyvern Stores £523 + VAT, invoice no. 3602
28 Nov	Sold goods to Raven Retailers Limited £187 + VAT, invoice no. 3603

You are to:

(a)   enter the above transactions in Pensax Products' sales day book for November 1997

(b)   record the accounting entries in Pensax Products' sales ledger and general ledger

5.3   The following details are the sales returns for Pensax Products for November 1997. They are to be

(a)   entered in the sales returns day book for November 1997

(b)   recorded in the sales ledger and general ledger (use the ledgers already prepared in the answer to Activity 5.2)

1997

10 Nov	Dines Stores returns goods £55 + VAT, credit note no. CN 831 is issued
14 Nov	Wyvern Stores returns goods £60 + VAT, credit note no. CN 832 is issued
19 Nov	Meadow Golf Club returns goods £46 + VAT, credit note no. CN 833 is issued
24 Nov	Teme Sports Limited returns goods £127 + VAT, credit note no. CN 834 is issued
28 Nov	Dines Stores returns goods £87 + VAT, credit note no. CN 835 is issued

5.4   John Green runs a wholesale nursery where he grows plants, shrubs and trees. These are sold on credit to garden centres, shops, and local authorities. His book-keeper records sales in an analysed sales day book including columns for VAT, plants, shrubs, trees. During April 1997 the following credit transactions took place:

1997

2 Apr	Sold trees to Wyvern Council £550 + VAT, invoice no. 2741
4 Apr	Sold plants to Mereford Garden Centre £345 + VAT, invoice no. 2742
7 Apr	Sold trees £155 and shrubs £265 (both + VAT) to JJ Gardening Services, invoice no. 2743
10 Apr	Sold shrubs to Mereford Garden Centre, £275 + VAT, invoice no. 2744
11 Apr	Sold plants to Dines Stores £127 + VAT, invoice no. 2745
15 Apr	Sold shrubs £127 and plants £352 (both + VAT) to Wyvern Council, invoice no. 2746
17 Apr	Sold plants to Harford Post Office £228 + VAT, invoice no. 2247
23 Apr	Sold trees to Mereford Garden Centre £175 + VAT, invoice no. 2748
25 Apr	Sold plants to Bourne Supplies £155 + VAT, invoice no. 2749
29 Apr	Sold trees £265 and plants £451 (both + VAT) to Mereford Garden Centre, invoice no. 2750

You are to:

•   enter the above transactions into the analysed day book of John Green

•   total the day book at 30 April

Note: Entries in the sales ledger and general ledger are not required.

NVQ coverage

unit 2 elements 1 & 3

- *entering invoices and credit notes into primary records*
- *entries into the ledger accounts*

6 ACCOUNTING FOR CREDIT PURCHASES AND PURCHASES RETURNS

Note: photocopiable accounts and daybooks are printed in the Appendix (see page 243).

> *In the activities which follow, the rate of Value Added Tax is to be calculated at the current rate (17.5% at the time of writing). When calculating VAT amounts, you should ignore fractions of a penny, ie round down to a whole penny.*
>
> *Leave the folio column blank, and do not use account numbers, unless otherwise stated.*

6.1 Anne Green owns a shop selling paint and decorating materials; she is registered for Value Added Tax. She has two suppliers, Wyper Limited (account no 301) and M Roper & Sons (account no 302). During the month of May 1997 Anne received the following business documents from her suppliers:

1997

2 May	Invoice no. 562 from M Roper & Sons for £190 + VAT
5 May	Invoice no. 82 from Wyper Limited for £200 + VAT
9 May	Invoice no. 86 from Wyper Limited for £210 + VAT
16 May	Invoice no. 580 from M Roper & Sons for £180 + VAT
19 May	Credit note no. 82 from M Roper & Sons for £30 + VAT
21 May	Invoice no. 91 from Wyper Limited for £240 + VAT
23 May	Credit note no. 6 from Wyper Limited for £40 + VAT
27 May	Invoice no. 589 from M Roper & Sons for £98 + VAT
28 May	Credit note no. 84 from M Roper & Sons for £38 + VAT

You are to:

(a)   enter the above transactions in Anne Green's purchases day book and purchases returns day book (to include folio columns) which are to be totalled at the end of May

(b)   record the accounting entries in Anne Green's purchases ledger and general ledger

6.2 The Oasis Trading Company records its credit purchases in an analysed day book with the following headings: goods for resale, printing, telephone, other expenses. The transactions for March 1997 are as follows:

1997

3 Mar	Bought goods for resale from Severn Valley Traders £255.50 + VAT, invoice no. X1247
4 Mar	Bought goods for resale from Mercian Suppliers £356.25 + VAT, invoice no. 7977
6 Mar	Received invoice no. Z495 for £136.95 + VAT from Print Services Ltd for printing
10 Mar	Bought goods for resale from D James Ltd £368.21 + VAT, invoice no. 2461

14 Mar	Received invoice no. 769431 for £218.25 + VAT from United Telecom for telephone costs
17 Mar	Received invoice no. A419 for £45.40 + VAT from Wyvern Garage for vehicle repairs
19 Mar	Bought goods for resale from A-Z Traders £496.84 + VAT, invoice no. AZ 7231
21 Mar	Received invoice no. 561742 for £154.65 + VAT from Saturn Communications for telephone costs
24 Mar	Received invoice no. 2761 for £151.20 + VAT from A J Knowles for decorating work
25 Mar	Bought goods for resale from Severn Valley Traders £357.24 + VAT, invoice no. X1299
28 Mar	Received invoice no. 597234 for £121.47 + VAT from Total Communications plc for telephone costs
31 Mar	Received invoice no. Z610 for £117.25 from Print Services Ltd for printing

You are to:

*   enter the above transactions into an analysed purchases day book
*   total the day book at 31 March

Note: Entries in the purchases ledger and general ledger are not required.

6.3   The following are the credit transactions of Eveshore Engineering Suppliers for the month of August 1997:

1997

1 Aug	Bought goods from Steel Suppliers £250 + VAT, their invoice no. A83
4 Aug	Bought goods from Howard Engineering £110 + VAT, their invoice no. 2014
5 Aug	Sold goods to Green Bros £295 + VAT, invoice no. 5678
6 Aug	Returned goods to Steel Suppliers £50 + VAT; credit note no. 412 received
7 Aug	Sold goods to G Gregory £305 + VAT, invoice no. 5679
11 Aug	Green Bros return goods £20 + VAT; credit note no. CN 771 issued
12 Aug	Bought goods from Howard Engineering £125 + VAT, their invoice no. 2107
14 Aug	Sold goods to Mereford Manufacturing £420 + VAT, invoice no. 5680
18 Aug	Bought goods from Birmingham Foundry £355 + VAT, their invoice no. BM2841
20 Aug	Mereford Manufacturing returns goods £25 + VAT; credit note no. CN 772 issued
21 Aug	Sold goods to Green Bros £250 + VAT, invoice no. 5681
25 Aug	Returned goods to Birmingham Foundry £75 + VAT; credit note no. BM 330 received
26 Aug	Bought goods from Steel Suppliers £125 + VAT, their invoice no. A107
28 AugS	Sold goods to G Gregory £258 + VAT, invoice no. 5682

You are to:

(a)   enter the above transactions in the appropriate day books of Eveshore Engineering Suppliers

(b)   record the accounting entries in Eveshore Engineering Suppliers' purchases ledger, sales ledger and general ledger

NVQ coverage

unit 2 elements 1 & 2

- *functions of a ledger system*
- *double-entry principles*
- *main types of account*

7 FURTHER ASPECTS OF DOUBLE -ENTRY ACCOUNTS

Note: photocopiable double-entry accounts are printed in the Appendix (see page 243).

7.1   Tom Griffiths has recently set up in business. He has made some errors in writing up his bank account. You are to set out the bank account as it should appear, and make the appropriate entries in the other accounts.

Dr			**Bank Account**			Cr
1997		£	1997			£
4 Mar	Office equipment	1,000	3 Mar	Capital		6,500
12 Mar	Drawings	175	5 Mar	Bank loan		2,500
			7 Mar	Wages		250
			10 Mar	Commission received		150
			12 Mar	Rent paid		200
			17 Mar	Van		6,000

Note: Tom Griffiths is not registered for Value Added Tax.

7.2   Enter the following transactions into the double-entry book-keeping accounts of Caroline Yates, who is registered for Value Added Tax:

1997

3 Nov	Started in business with capital of £75,000 in the bank
4 Nov	Bought a photocopier for £2,400 + VAT, paying by cheque
7 Nov	Received a bank loan of £70,000
10 Nov	Bought office premises £130,000, paying by cheque
12 Nov	Paid rates of £3,000, by cheque
14 Nov	Bought office fittings £1,520 + VAT, paying by cheque
17 Nov	Received commission of £400 + VAT, in cash

18 Nov	Drawings in cash £125	
20 Nov	Paid wages £250, by cheque	
24 Nov	Paid £100 of cash into the bank	
25 Nov	Returned some of the office fittings (unsuitable) and received a refund cheque for £200 + VAT	
28 Nov	Received commission £200 + VAT, by cheque	

Note: Use the current rate of Value Added Tax (17.5% at the time of writing).

7.3 The following account appears in the books of Peter Singh:

Dr			Bank Account				Cr
1997		£		1997			£
1 Jan	Capital	10,000		2 Jan	Office equipment		3,000
3 Jan	Commission received	500		2 Jan	Rates		1,500
7 Jan	Bank loan	2,500		6 Jan	Cash		250
				7 Jan	Drawings		500
				8 Jan	Van		7,500

Taking each transaction in turn, describe to Peter Singh the transaction undertaken by his business, and explain the other account in which each appears in his double-entry accounts.

Note: Peter Singh is not registered for Value Added Tax.

NVQ coverage

unit 2

- operation of accounting systems
- double-entry principles

8 BALANCING ACCOUNTS AND THE TRIAL BALANCE

Note: photocopiable accounts, daybooks and a blank statement are printed in the Appendix (see page 243).

8.1 The following are the business transactions of Robert Jefferson, a bookshop owner, for the months of January and February 1997:

Transactions for January

1997

1 Jan	Started in business with capital of £5,000 in the bank
2 Jan	Paid rent on premises £200, by cheque
3 Jan	Bought shop fittings £2,000, by cheque
6 Jan	Bought stock of books £2,500, on credit from Northam Publishers
8 Jan	Book sales £1,200, paid into bank
9 Jan	Book sales £1,000, paid into bank
13 Jan	Bought books £5,000, on credit from Broadheath Books
15 Jan	Book sales £1,500 to Teme School, a cheque being received
17 Jan	Book sales, £1,250, paid into bank
20 Jan	Bought books from Financial Publications £2,500, by cheque
23 Jan	Teme School returned unsuitable books £580, cheque refund sent
30 Jan	Sold books on credit to Wyvern College, £1,095

Transactions for February

1997

3 Feb	Book sales £2,510, paid into bank
5 Feb	Paid rent on premises £200, by cheque
7 Feb	Bought shop fittings £1,385, by cheque
10 Feb	Book sales £3,875, paid into bank
11 Feb	Sent cheque, £2,500, to Northam Publishers
13 Feb	Bought books £1,290, on credit from Northam Publishers
14 Feb	Sent cheque, £5,000, to Broadheath Books
17 Feb	Book sales £1,745, paid into bank

18 Feb	Wyvern College returned books, £250
21 Feb	Book sales £1,435, paid into bank
24 Feb	Bought books £1,250, on credit from Associated Publishers
28 Feb	Book sales £3,900, paid into bank

You are to:

(a)   Record the January transactions in his double-entry accounts. Each account is to be balanced at 31 January 1997

(b)   Draw up a trial balance at 31 January 1997

(c)   Record the February transactions in his double-entry accounts. Each account is to be balanced at 28 February 1997

(d)   Draw up a trial balance at 28 February 1997

Notes:

• day books are not required

• Robert Jefferson is not registered for VAT

8.2   A friend, who is just beginning her studies of book-keeping comments:

•   "if the trial balance totals agree it is proof that the book-keeping entries are 100 per cent correct"

•   "I wouldn't know where to start looking if the trial balance totals did not agree"

Reply to your friend.

8.3   Kevin Kemp works in the accounts department of a manufacturing company that produces specialist engineering components for the car industry. The company, Turner & Sons Limited, Unit 10, Valley Road Industrial Estate, Mereford, MR1 5PQ, has just computerised its accounting system.

The accountant, Mr T Worth, has instructed Kevin that for the first few months, while the accounts are being produced by computer, he is to keep separate manual records of the company's transactions. Kevin's instructions are to record only the documents issued and received; the accountant will record manually cash and bank transactions.

The computer accounting system was introduced on 1 March 1997. At that date, Turner & Sons Limited had the following accounts in the purchases and sales ledgers:

Purchases ledger

Ace Forgings Limited, balance	£550.00 credit
Round Tubes Limited, balance	£610.00 credit
Bright Metal Company Limited, balance	£120.00 credit

Sales ledger

Toyisson Motors plc, balance	£870.00 debit
Portland Vehicles Limited, balance	£940.00 debit
Bramhall Vehicles plc, balance	£340.00 debit

Turner & Sons Limited also had the following balances in the general ledger on 1 March 1997:

- purchases   £4,050.00 debit
- sales   £9,600.00 credit
- Value Added Tax   £832.50 credit

During the first month that the computer was operational (March 1997), Kevin recorded the invoices issued and received shown on pages 43 to 52.

You are to assume the role of Kevin (or Karen) Kemp and undertake the following tasks:

(a) Enter the invoices in the appropriate day books and, at the end of March, total the books.

(b) Open the accounts in Turner & Sons Limited's ledger system with the balance on 1 March 1997. Record the accounting entries from the primary accounting records into the appropriate account in Turner & Sons Limited's sales ledger, purchases ledger and general ledger. The accounts needed are:

- Sales Ledger – accounts for each customer
- Purchases Ledger – accounts for each supplier
- General Ledger – sales account, purchases account, VAT account

(c) Balance each account at 31 March 1997.

(d) Assuming that no money settlement has been forwarded or received during March 1997:

- draw up and complete statements of account for Turner & Sons Limited's customers
- compile a list of the outstanding balances Turner & Sons Limited owes its suppliers
- compile a list of the outstanding balances Turner & Sons Limited is owed by its customers

Note: photocopiable accounts, daybooks and a blank statement are printed in the Appendix (see page 243).

No. 1011

INVOICE

| TURNER & SONS LTD |
| Unit 10 |
| Valley Road Industrial Estate |
| MEREFORD |
| MR1 5PQ |

Tel/Fax: 01605 732491
VAT Reg No 407 8693 82

To:

Toyisson Motors plc
Star Way
RIPTON
RP4 7JH

Date/Tax Point: 3 Mar 1997

Customer Order No. 5871/91

Customer Account No. T 0141

Quantity	Description	Unit Price £ p	Total Amount £ p
20	Mouldings: type ABC123	10 00	200 00
		Total Goods	200 00
		Value Added Tax	35 00
		Total Due	235 00

Terms: Net Monthly
E & OE

INVOICE

No. 1012

**TURNER & SONS LTD
Unit 10
Valley Road Industrial Estate
MEREFORD
MR1 5PQ**

Tel/Fax: 01605 732491
VAT Reg No 407 8693 82

To:

Bramhall Vehicles plc
140-144 Bramley Way
HALLTOWN
HL2 8AH

Date/Tax Point: 4 Mar 1997

Customer Order No.   27469/01

Customer Account No. B 0103

Quantity	Description	Unit Price £ p	Total Amount £ p
250	Mouldings: type BV861	2 00	500 00
		Total Goods	500 00
		Value Added Tax	87 50
		Total Due	587 50

Terms: Net Monthly
E & OE

INVOICE

Ace Forgings Ltd
Ace Works Tipton Way
PUDLEY PY3 8TD

Tel/Fax: 01681 234966
VAT Reg No 684 9143 21

Invoice to

TURNER & SONS LTD
Unit 10
Valley Road Industrial Estate
MEREFORD MR1 5PQ

Invoice no: 87

Account: 428

Date/tax point: 6 Mar 1997

Order no: TS 6851

Quantity	Description	Unit Price £ p	Total Amount £ p
200 metres	Steel section: type 457	4 00	800 00
	Total Goods		800 00
	Value Added Tax		140 00
	Total Due		940 00

TERMS

NET MONTHLY

CARRIAGE PAID

E & OE

INVOICE

Round Tubes Ltd
The Tube Works
Terry Hill Industrial Estate
BARLASTON PY3 1AJ
Tel/Fax: 01681 794238
VAT Reg No 986 3217 64

Invoice to

TURNER & SONS LTD
Unit 10
Valley Road Industrial Estate
MEREFORD MR1 5PQ

Invoice no: 101
Account: TU 317
Date/tax point: 7 Mar 1997
Order no: TS 6852

Quantity	Description	Unit Price £ p	Total Amount £ p
100 lengths	Plate steel tube: type OJ/157	3 00	300 00
	Total Goods		300 00
	Value Added Tax		52 50
	Total Due		352 50

TERMS

NET MONTHLY

CARRIAGE PAID

E & OE

No. 1013

INVOICE

| TURNER & SONS LTD |
| Unit 10 |
| Valley Road Industrial Estate |
| MEREFORD |
| MR1 5PQ |

Tel/Fax: 01605 732491
VAT Reg No 407 8693 82

To:

Bramhall Vehicles plc
140-144 Bramley Way
HALLTOWN
HL2 8AH

Date/Tax Point: 10 Mar 1997

Customer Order No. 27521/01

Customer Account No. B 0103

Quantity	Description	Unit Price £ p	Total Amount £ p
50	Gear units: type 747/21	20 00	1,000 00
	Total Goods		1,000 00
	Value Added Tax		175 00
	Total Due		1,175 00

Terms: Net Monthly
E & OE

INVOICE

No. 1014

TURNER & SONS LTD
Unit 10
Valley Road Industrial Estate
MEREFORD
MR1 5PQ

Tel/Fax: 01605 732491
VAT Reg No 407 8693 82

To:

Portland Vehicles Ltd
Portland Works
BRIDGTON
BR4 1AP

Date/Tax Point: 18 Mar 1997

Customer Order No. 386/17

Customer Account No. P 0170

Quantity	Description	Unit Price £ p	Total Amount £ p
75	Gear units: type 747/25	20 00	1,500 00
	Total Goods		1,500 00
	Value Added Tax		262 50
	Total Due		1,762 50

Terms: Net Monthly
E & OE

INVOICE

No. 1015

TURNER & SONS LTD
Unit 10
Valley Road Industrial Estate
MEREFORD
MR1 5PQ

Tel/Fax: 01605 732491
VAT Reg No 407 8693 82

To:

Toyisson Motors plc
Star Way
RIPTON
RP4 7JH

Date/Tax Point: 25 Mar 1997

Customer Order No. 6010/91

Customer Account No. T 0141

Quantity	Description	Unit Price £ p	Total Amount £ p
120	Mouldings: type ABC123	10 00	1,200 00
	Total Goods		1,200 00
	Value Added Tax		210 00
	Total Due		1,410 00

Terms: Net Monthly
E & OE

Invoice no. 58

BRIGHT METAL COMPANY LTD
Unit 91, Cotheridge Industrial Estate
CARPMINSTER   CA3 4JT

Tel/Fax: 01724 683910
VAT Reg No: 226 4932 71

Invoice to

TURNER & SONS LTD
Unit 10
Valley Road Industrial Estate
MEREFORD   MR1 5PQ

Account: 4271

Date/tax point: 14 Mar 1997

Order no: TS 6853

Quantity	Description	Unit Price £ p	Total Amount £ p
200	Plated pressings: type 6/09	3 00	600 00
	Total Goods		600 00
	Value Added Tax		105 00
	Total Due		705 00

TERMS

NET MONTHLY

CARRIAGE PAID

E & OE

INVOICE

Ace Forgings Ltd
Ace Works Tipton Way
PUDLEY PY3 8TD

Tel/Fax: 01681 234966
VAT Reg No 684 9143 21

Invoice to

TURNER & SONS LTD
Unit 10
Valley Road Industrial Estate
MEREFORD MR1 5PQ

Invoice no: 96
Account: 428
Date/tax point: 25 Mar 1997
Order no: TS 6854

Quantity	Description	Unit Price £ p	Total Amount £ p
100 metres	Steel section: type 457	4 00	400 00
	Total Goods		400 00
	Value Added Tax		70 00
	Total Due		470 00

TERMS

NET MONTHLY

CARRIAGE PAID

E & OE

INVOICE

Round Tubes Ltd
The Tube Works
Terry Hill Industrial Estate
BARLASTON PY3 1AJ

Tel/Fax: 01681 794238
VAT Reg No 986 3217 64

Invoice to

TURNER & SONS LTD
Unit 10
Valley Road Industrial Estate
MEREFORD   MR1 5PQ

Invoice no:	109
Account:	TU 317
Date/tax point:	31 Mar 1997
Order no:	TS 6855

Quantity	Description	Unit Price £ p	Total Amount £ p
70 lengths	Steel tube: type OP/191	2 00	140 00
		Total Goods	140 00
		Value Added Tax	24 50
		Total Due	164 50

TERMS

NET MONTHLY

CARRIAGE PAID

E & OE

9 DEBTORS AND CREDITORS

NVQ coverage

unit 2 element 3

- dealing with debtors' accounts
- dealing with creditors' accounts

Note: photocopiable double-entry accounts and a journal page are printed in the Appendix (see page 243).

9.1 The sales ledger of Morrisson Traders contains the following account:

Dr			**Discount Stores**			Cr
1997		£	1997			£
11 Apr	Sales	1,476	15 May	Bank		1,476
18 Apr	Sales	854	30 May	Bank		854
6 May	Sales	1,008				
9 May	Sales	491				
13 June	Sales	897				

Complete the following age analysis:

Discount Stores			
Age analysis at 16 June 1997			
Balance	Up to 1 month	1 to 2 months	Over 2 months
£	£	£	£
....	....	....	....

9.2 A friend of yours, Natasha Williams, runs a catering business which supplies food and drink to companies for special events. You keep the 'books' for the business, which is not registered for VAT.

Natasha tells you about a customer, Mereford Marketing, for whom she provided catering for their stand at the 'Four Counties Show'. The details are:

10 Jul 1997   Invoice for £350 sent to Mereford Marketing

7 Aug 1997   Cheque received for £300

10 Sep 1997 Cheque received for £20

It is now 18 December 1997 and Natasha doesn't think she will be able to collect the remaining amount due and asks you to write off the balance of the account as a bad debt.

You are to show:

- the journal entry made on 18 December
- the transactions on Mereford Marketing's account in Natasha's sales ledger
- the bad debts written off account in Natasha's general ledger

9.3   You work as an assistant in the accounts department of JR Catering Limited, a contract caterer. Your supervisor has asked you to obtain an aged debtors' schedule from the computer. The printout shown below is the first page of the schedule. An asterisk shows an account that is over its credit limit. JR Catering allows up to 30 days credit to all its customers.

Write a memorandum (dated 7 December 1997) to the accounts supervisor, Lorna Jones, setting out:

(a)   the accounts that may be a source of trouble, and why

(b)   corrective action that the business might take

JR CATERING LTD		Sales Ledger - Account Balances (Aged)					Date: 301197
A/C	Account Name	Credit Limit	Balance	Current	30 Days	60 Days	Older
----	--------------------	----------------	-----------	----------	-----------	-----------	-------
201	Merrion & Co	1000.00	164.50	164.50	0.00	0.00	0.00
202	Kingfisher Ltd	750.00	376.00	376.00	0.00	0.00	0.00
204	I Marchand*	1000.00	1632.75	799.00	0.00	833.75	0.00
205	Compusoft Ltd	2000.00	1926.88	1880.00	46.88	0.00	0.00
208	R Winbeck	750.00	499.38	499.38	0.00	0.00	0.00
	Totals :	5500.00	4599.51	3718.88	46.88	833.75	0.00

9.4   The following account appears in your firm's purchases ledger:

Dr				William Shaw Limited			Cr
1997			£	1997			£
10 Mar	Purchases returns		156	1 Mar	Balance b/d		640
12 Mar	Bank		624	4 Mar	Purchases		756
	Discount		16	20 Mar	Purchases		845
25 Mar	Purchases returns		45				
30 Mar	Bank		780				
	Discount		20				

During the first week of April, the following statement of account was received from William Shaw Limited:

date	details	debit	credit	balance
1997		£	£	£
1 Mar	Balance b/d			1,080
2 Mar	Invoice 2841	756		1,836
6 Mar	Payment received		429	
	Discount allowed		11	1,396
10 Mar	Credit note 347		156	1,240
14 Mar	Payment received		624	
	Discount allowed		16	600
18 Mar	Invoice 3017	845		1,445
25 Mar	Credit note 357		45	1,400
29 Mar	Invoice 3278	1,027		2,427

You are to:

(a)   Reconcile the opening balance of William Shaw Limited's account at 1 March in your purchases ledger with the statement balance at that date

(b)   Balance the account in your purchases ledger at 31 March 1997

(c)   Reconcile the balance on your purchases ledger account at 31 March 1997 with that shown on the statement

NVQ coverage

unit 2 element 3

- reconciling the sales ledger with the control acount
- reconciling the purchases ledger with the control acount

Note: photocopiable double-entry accounts are printed in the Appendix (see page 243).

10 CONTROL ACCOUNTS

10.1 Would the following errors cause a difference between the balance of the sales ledger control account and the total of the balances in the sales ledger?

(a) The sales day book was overcast by £100.

(b) The amount of a sales invoice was debited to the account of Wyvern Traders instead of Wyvern Tiling.

(c) An invoice for £54 was recorded in the sales day book as £45.

10.2 Mereford Manufacturing Company Limited maintains a sales ledger control account in its general (nominal) ledger as part of its double-entry system. Individual accounts for customers are kept on a memorandum basis in a separate sales ledger.

On 1 November 1997 the sales ledger contains the following accounts:

A Abercrombie	balance £643.29 debit
Burton and Company	balance £1,472.41 debit
H Haig	balance £462.28 debit
T Norton	balance £392.48 debit
Shipley Limited	balance £68.87 debit
Yarnold and Sons Limited	balance £976.18 debit

The following transactions took place during November:

4 Nov	Sold goods on credit to A Abercrombie £225 + VAT, and T Norton £380 + VAT
5 Nov	H Haig settled his account in full by cheque
7 Nov	T Norton returned goods £151 + VAT
11 Nov	Yarnold and Sons Limited settled an invoice for £292.65 by cheque after deducting £6.25 cash discount
13 Nov	Sold goods on credit to Burton and Company £775 + VAT, and T Norton £195 + VAT
14 Nov	A Abercrombie returns goods £45 + VAT
17 Nov	Sold goods on credit to Yarnold and Sons Limited £458 + VAT
18 Nov	A Abercrombie settles her account in full by cheque after deducting £16.27 cash discount
21 Nov	Transferred the balance of T Norton's account to his account in the purchases ledger
25 Nov	Sold goods on credit to A Abercrombie £495 + VAT, and T Norton £169 + VAT
28 Nov	Wrote off the account of Shipley Limited as a bad debt

You are to:

(a) write up the personal accounts in the sales ledger of Mereford Manufacturing for November 1997, balancing them at the end of the month

(b) prepare a sales ledger control account for November 1997, balancing it at the end of the month

(c) reconcile the control account balance with the debtors' accounts at 1 November and 30 November 1997

Note: Mereford Manufacturing Company is registered for VAT; day books are not required.

10.3 Mereford Manufacturing Company Limited maintains a purchases ledger control account in its general (nominal) ledger as part of its double-entry system. Individual accounts for suppliers are kept on a memorandum basis in a separate purchases ledger.

On 1 November 1997 the purchases ledger contains the following accounts:

Bakewell Limited	balance £476.81 credit
Don Edge and Company	balance £1,107.52 credit
M Lister	balance £908.04 credit
T Norton	balance £543.21 credit
Percival and Company	balance £250.49 credit
Trent Supplies plc	balance £749.25 credit
Vector Metals Limited	balance £397.64 credit

The following transactions took place during November:

5 Nov	Bought goods on credit from Trent Supplies £179 + VAT, and Percival and Company £352 + VAT
7 Nov	Paid the balance of M Lister's account by cheque after deducting £15.34 cash discount
10 Nov	Bought goods on credit from T Norton £450 + VAT, and Vector Metals £370 + VAT
14 Nov	Paid by cheque an invoice from Don Edge and Company for £585.30 after deducting £12.50 cash discount
17 Nov	Returned goods to Percival and Company £28 + VAT
19 Nov	Bought goods on credit from Bakewell Limited £255 + VAT, and M Lister £302 + VAT
20 Nov	Paid Vector Metals Limited a cheque for the balance of the account
21 Nov	Transfer of debit balance of £890.68 in the sales ledger to T Norton's account in the purchases ledger
26 Nov	Returned goods to Vector Metals Limited £68 + VAT

You are to:

(a)   write up the personal accounts in the purchases ledger of Mereford Manufacturing for November 1997, balancing them at the end of the month

(b)   prepare a purchases ledger control account for November 1997, balancing it at the end of the month

(c)   reconcile the control account balance with the creditors' accounts at 1 November and 30 November 1997

Note: Mereford Manufacturing Company is registered for VAT; day books are not required.

10.4   Stourminster Limited uses control accounts for its purchases ledger and sales ledger. At 1 September 1997 the balances of the control accounts were:

	Debit	Credit
	£	£
Purchases ledger	128	65,027
Sales ledger	106,943	558

The following transactions took place during September 1997:

	£
Credit purchases	137,248
Credit sales	179,984
Sales returns	2,081
Purchases returns	6,349
Cash/cheques received from customers	163,481
Cash/cheques paid to suppliers	125,636
Customers' cheques dishonoured	357
Discount allowed	2,549
Discount received	1,832
Bad debts written off	528
Transfer of a credit balance from the purchases ledger to the sales ledger	2,086

At 30 September 1997, there were debit balances in the purchases ledger of £479 and credit balances in the sales ledger of £694

You are to:

•   prepare the purchases ledger control account and sales ledger control account at Stourminster Limited for September 1997

•   balance the accounts at 30 September 1997

11 THE JOURNAL

NVQ coverage

unit 2 elements 3 & 4

- adjustments to debtors' accounts

- adjustments to creditors' accounts

Note: photocopiable double-entry accounts and a journal page are printed in the Appendix (see page 243).

11.1 The purchase of £20 of stationery has been debited to office equipment account. This is:

(a)   an error of original entry

(b)   an error of principle

(c)   a mispost/error of commission

(d)   a reversal of entries

Answer (a) or (b) or (c) or (d)

11.2 A credit purchase of £63 from T Billington has been entered in the accounts as £36. This is:

(a)   a reversal of entries

(b)   an error of original entry

(c)   a compensating error

(d)   an error of omission

Answer (a) or (b) or (c) or (d)

11.3 A credit sale of £100 to L Jarvis has been credited to Jarvis' account and debited to sales account in error. Which of the following entries will correct the error?

	Debit		Credit	
(a)	Sales	£100	L Jarvis	£100
(b)	L Jarvis	£100	Sales	£100
(c)	Sales	£100	L Jarvis	£100
	Sales	£100	L Jarvis	£100
(d)	L Jarvis	£100	Sales	£100
	L Jarvis	£100	Sales	£100

Answer (a) or (b) or (c) or (d)

11.4 You have recently taken over writing up the double-entry accounts of B Brick (Builders). You have found a number of errors made by the previous book-keeper as follows:

(a)   Credit purchase of goods for £85 from J Stone has not been entered in the accounts

(b)   A cheque for £155 received from Roger Williams, a debtor, has been credited to the account of another debtor, William Rogers

(c)   Diesel fuel costing £30 has been debited to vehicles account

(d)   A credit sale for £154 to T Potter has been entered in the accounts as £145

(e)   The total of purchases returns day book has been overcast by £100 as has wages account

You are to take each error in turn and:
- state the type of error
- show the correcting journal entry

Notes:
- VAT is to be ignored
- B Brick (Builders) does not use control accounts in the book-keeping system

11.5 Tracey Truslove is the book-keeper for Mereford Traders Limited. At 30 June 1997 she is unable to balance the trial balance. The difference, £221 credit, is placed to a suspense account in the general ledger pending further investigation.

The following errors are later found:

(a)   Purchases account is undercast by £100.

(b)   A cheque from L Lewis, a debtor, for £95 has been recorded in the personal account as £59.

(c)   Rent received of £205 has been debited to both the rent received account and the bank account.

(d)   Vehicles expenses of £125 have not been entered in the expenses account.

You are to:
- make journal entries to correct the errors
- show the suspense account after the errors have been corrected
- following receipt of a memorandum from the accounts supervisor, make a further journal entry to write off as a bad debt the balance of £80 on the account of L Branksome, a debtor

Notes:
- VAT is to be ignored
- Mereford Traders does not use control accounts in its book-keeping system

NVQ coverage

unit 1 element 1

- *record and bank monies received*

12 RECEIVING AND RECORDING PAYMENTS

WORKBOOK ACTIVITIES

12.1 You are operating a cash till at the firm where you work. Today the cash float at the start of the day is £22.30, made up as follows:

2 x £5 notes	=	£10.00
6 x £1 coins	=	£6.00
6 x 50p coins	=	£3.00
8 x 20p coins	=	£1.60
10 x 10p coins	=	£1.00
8 x 5p coins	=	£0.40
12 x 2p coins	=	£0.24
6 x 1p coins	=	£0.06
		£22.30

The following are the sales which pass through the till today:

		Amount of sales £	Notes and/or coin tendered
Customer	1	7.50	£10 note
	2	3.38	£5 note
	3	2.29	two £1 coins and a 50p coin
	4	18.90	£20 note
	5	6.04	£10 note, £1 coin, two 2p coins
	6	26.36	three £10 notes
	7	4.30	four £1 coins and a 50p coin

You are to:

(a) state the amount of change to be given to each customer

(b) state the notes and/or coin that will be given in change, using the minimum number possible

(c) calculate the denominations of notes and coin that will remain in the till at the end of the day

(d)   retain a cash float which does not exceed £30.00 (show the denominations of notes and coin); the remainder of the cash is to be banked (show denominations)

(e)   prepare a summary of the day's transactions in the following form:

		£
	cash float at start	22.30
plus	sales made during the day	————
equals	amount of cash held at end of day	
less	cash float retained for next day	————
	amount banked	════════

12.2   You work as an accounts assistant in the Accounts Department of Mercia Pumps Ltd, Unit 13, Severn Trading Estate, Mereford MR3 4GF.   Today is 3 April 1998. In the morning's post are a number of cheques enclosed with remittance advices. These cheques are illustrated below.

Examine the cheques carefully, and identify any problems, and state what action (if any) you will take, and why. Draft letters where appropriate for your Manager's (Mrs D Strong) signature.

You note from your records that the addresses are as follows:

(a)   The Accounts Department, A & S Systems, 5 High Street, Mereford MR1 2JF

(b)   Mrs P Thorne, Hillside Cottage, Mintfield, MR4 9HG

(c)   The Accounts Department, C Darwin Ltd, 89 Baker Street, Mereford MR2 6RG

(d)   Mr I M King, 56 Beaconsfield Drive, Pershore MR7 5GF

(a)

Eastern Bank PLC Broadfield Branch 107 Market Street, Broadfield BR1 9NG	date *30 March* 19 *98*	44-77-09
Pay *Mercia Pumps Limited* ————————————————		only
Four hundred pounds only ————————	Account payee only	£ *400.00*
		A & S SYSTEMS

989954   44 77 09   21907634

(b)

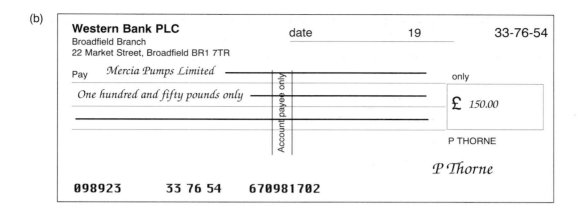

Western Bank PLC
Broadfield Branch
22 Market Street, Broadfield BR1 7TR

date   19   33-76-54

Pay   *Mercia Pumps Limited*   only

One hundred and fifty pounds only

£ *150.00*

Account payee only

P THORNE

P Thorne

098923   33 76 54   670981702

(c)

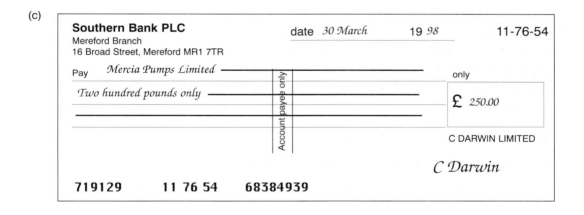

Southern Bank PLC
Mereford Branch
16 Broad Street, Mereford MR1 7TR

date *30 March*   19 *98*   11-76-54

Pay   *Mercia Pumps Limited*   only

Two hundred pounds only

£ *250.00*

Account payee only

C DARWIN LIMITED

C Darwin

719129   11 76 54   68384939

(d)   Mr King has made the cheque payable to your Sales Director, John Hopkins, who says he is happy to endorse the cheque over to the company.

Northern Bank PLC
Mereford Branch
28 High Street, Mereford MR1 8FD

date *30 March*   19 *98*   22-01-59

Pay   *John Hopkins*   only

Sixty pounds only

£ *60.00*

Account payee only

I KING

I M King

123456   22 01 59   37537147

12.3 You work as a cashier at Cripplegate DIY store. The date today is January 20 1998. You deal with a number of customers who wish to make payment using cheques and cheque card. What action would you take in the following circumstances, and why?

(a) Card limit £100, expiry June 1998, code 11-76-54. The name on the card is J E Drew. The lady explains that she has just got married, and Drew is her maiden name.

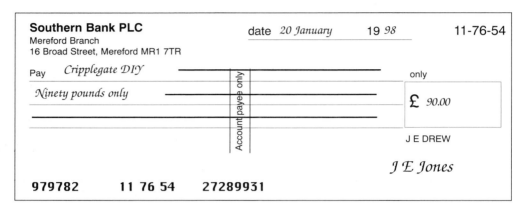

(b) Card limit £100, expiry May 1998, code 22-01-59. Mr King wants to buy some garden furniture costing £150.95. He has made out the following cheques in advance.

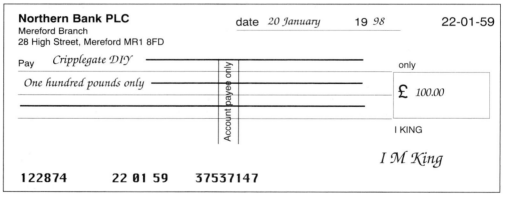

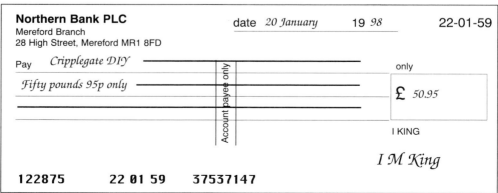

(c)   Card limit £200, expiry April 1998, code 33-76-54. The cheque card is handed to you in a plastic wallet and the signature on the card does not quite tally with the signature on the cheque. The customer says that he has sprained his wrist and this has affected his writing.

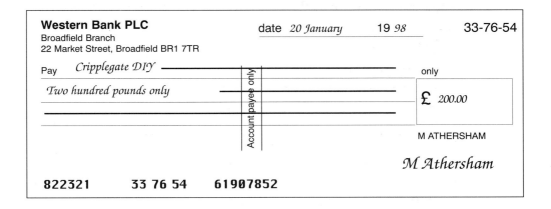

(d)   Card limit £200, expiry August 1998, code 88-76-54. Mrs Blackstone is in a great hurry and asks you to be as quick as you can. She seems to be rather agitated. The signature on the cheque matches the signature on the card and everything else seems to be in order.

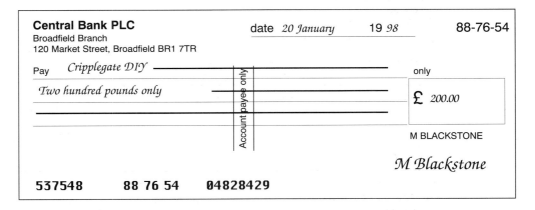

NVQ coverage

unit 1 element 1

- *record and bank monies received*

13 PAYING INTO THE BANK

WORKBOOK ACTIVITIES

13.1 You are working in the accounts department of Martley Fruits Limited, Maytree Farm, Martley MR7 2LX. Part of your job is to deal with the cheques received in the post, and to prepare those cheques for banking. During the course of a working day you deal with a number of cheques, some of which may cause problems. Your supervisor, Mark Tucker, asks you to identify the problems, and state in each case how you would deal with them. Write down your answers using the schedule on the next page.

	customer	amount	comments
(a)	Henry Young & Co	£1,245	you need to find out whether this cheque is to be paid before you can despatch the goods – rapid clearance is required
(b)	J Maxwell Ltd	£124.90	you receive this cheque from the bank; it is marked 'Refer to Drawer'
(c)	Ivor Longway	£342.90	the date on the cheque is three months old
(d)	Ned Morgan	£837.89	the date on the cheque is ten months old
(e)	Lisa Jones	£90.00	you receive this cheque from the bank; the cheque is marked 'Post dated'; on inspecting the cheque you see that the cheque is dated three months in the future
(f)	N Patel	£78.00	you receive this cheque from the bank; it is marked 'Payment Countermanded by order of Drawer'
(g)	N Trebbiano	£78.98	there is no crossing on the cheque

When you have checked your answer schedule with your tutor you are to draft appropriate letters for your supervisor's signature to the following customers (use today's date):

J Maxwell Ltd, 67 The Circus, Bradstreet, BD5 8GY

Ned Morgan, 72 Malvern Crescent, Milton Park, MR6 2CS

Lisa Jones, c/o The Kings Arms, Leatherton, MR6 9SD

customer	problem	solution
Henry Young & Co		
J Maxwell Ltd		
Ivor Longway		
Ned Morgan		
Lisa Jones		
N Patel		
N Trebbiano		

13.2 You are working in the Accounts Department of Wyvern (Office Products) Limited and have been handed the latest bank statement by your supervisor, Alfred Hunter. He asks you to sort out two queries:

- The credit paid in on 1 April appears as £485.02; your paying slip shows the total as £485.04.

- What is the unpaid item on 7 April? Nothing has yet been received from the bank.

The relevant documentation appears on this and the next page.

NATIONAL BANK PLC

Statement of Account

Branch: Mereford

Account: Wyvern (Office Products) Ltd
Account no 01099124   Sheet no 105   Statement date 10 Apr 1998

Date	Details	Withdrawals	Deposits	Balance
1998		£	£	£
1 Apr	Balance brought forward			1,300.00 Cr
1 Apr	Credit		2,000.00	3,300.00 Cr
1 Apr	BACS Prime Hotels Ltd		2,000.00	5,300.00 Cr
1 Apr	Credit		485.02	5,785.02 Cr
3 Apr	Bank charges	70.00		5,715.02 Cr
7 Apr	Unpaid cheque	2,000.00		3,715.02 Cr
10 Apr	Cheque 123745	1,860.00		1,855.02 Cr

SO Standing Order **DD** Direct Debit   **TR** Transfer   **BGC** Bank giro credit **BACS** Automated transfer

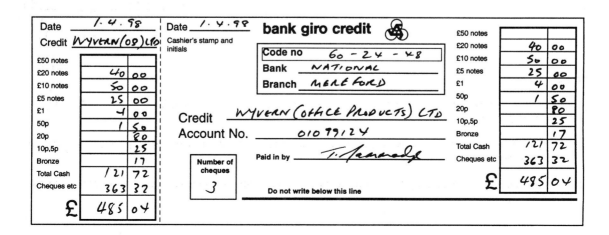

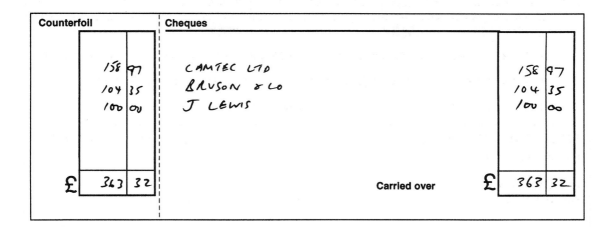

Counterfoil		Cheques	
158	97	CAMTEC LTD	158	97
104	35	BRUSON & CO	104	35
100	00	J LEWIS	100	00
£ 363	32	Carried over	£ 363	32

REMITTANCE ADVICE
BRUSON & CO
25 Melody Chambers, Gloucester GL1 2RF
Tel 01452 37232182 Fax 01452 37234496

Wyvern (Office Products) Ltd
12 Lower Hyde Street
Mereford MR1 2JF

Cheque No	774474
Date	18 February 1998
Account	2947

date	our ref.	your ref.	amount	discount	payment
16.3.98	8274	35357	104.33	00.00	104.33

cheque value £ 104.33

You are to

(a) Write a memorandum to your supervisor explaining what has happened in relation to the paying-in slip and the bank statement.

(b) Write down in numbered points what actions you think should be taken as a result of the mistake on the credit.

(c) Write down in numbered points what actions you think should be taken as a result of the unpaid cheque.

NVQ coverage

unit 1 element 2

• *make and record payments*

14 MAKING AND RECORDING PAYMENTS

WORKBOOK ACTIVITIES

14.1 You work as an assistant in the accounts department of A & S Systems Limited, computer consultants. Your job is to pay purchase invoices. Your file contains 12 invoices which have all been approved for payment.

The company writes out cheques in settlement of suppliers' invoices every Friday. It is company policy to pay strictly according to the terms of the invoice and to take advantage of cash discounts whenever possible. Today is Friday 27 March 1998.

You have been on holiday for a fortnight and someone else has done your job the last two Fridays. Your supervisor suggests you check carefully to make sure your file is brought up to date and all outstanding invoices are settled, as he suspects some may have been overlooked.

You are to select the invoices due for payment and calculate the amount due on those invoices, taking into account any cash discount. A summary of the invoices is shown below.

invoice date	supplier	terms	net	VAT	invoice total
			£	£	£
11.02.98	James Smith Ltd	30 days	456.89	79.95	536.84
13.02.98	R Singh	30 days*	1,200.00	204.75	1,404.75
24.02.98	John Hopkins	30 days	230.75	40.38	271.13
24.02.98	Mereford Supplies	60 days	235.00	41.12	276.12
2.03.98	E Ragle Ltd	30 days	345.89	60.53	406.42
23.03.98	Meteor Ltd	30 days*	2,400.00	409.50	2,809.50
16.02.98	Helen Jarvis	30 days	109.00	19.07	128.07
17.02.98	Martley Electronics	60 days	245.00	42.87	287.87
24.03.98	Jones & Co	30 days*	950.00	162.09	1,112.09
20.02.98	J Marvell	30 days	80.95	14.16	95.11
19.02.98	K Nott	60 days	457.50	80.06	537.56
20.03.98	V Williams	30 days	1,250.00	218.75	1,468.75

* These invoices are marked '2.5% cash discount for settlement within 7 days'.

14.2 Complete the cheques shown on this and the next page in settlement of the invoices you have decided to pay. The date today is 27 March 1998. You will not sign the cheques; this will be done by two authorised signatories.

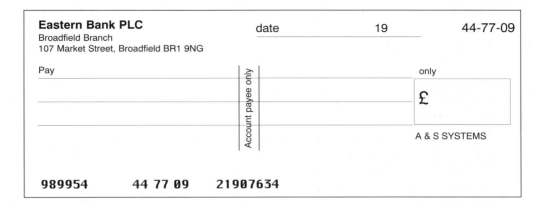

Eastern Bank PLC
Broadfield Branch
107 Market Street, Broadfield BR1 9NG

date _____ 19 _____   44-77-09

Pay

only

Account payee only

£

A & S SYSTEMS

989954   44 77 09   21907634

Eastern Bank PLC
Broadfield Branch
107 Market Street, Broadfield BR1 9NG

date _____ 19 _____   44-77-09

Pay

only

Account payee only

£

A & S SYSTEMS

989955   44 77 09   21907634

Eastern Bank PLC
Broadfield Branch
107 Market Street, Broadfield BR1 9NG

date _____ 19 _____   44-77-09

Pay

only

Account payee only

£

A & S SYSTEMS

989956   44 77 09   21907634

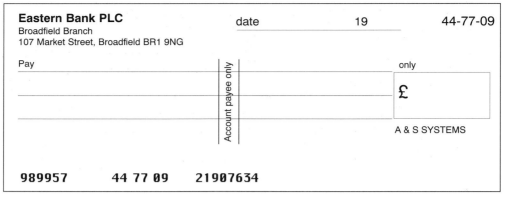

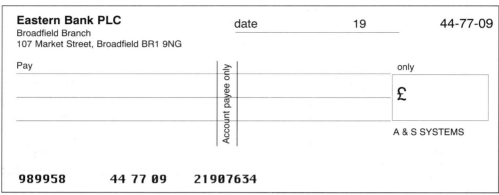

14.3 On 27 March 1998 your supervisor also asks you to arrange three payments: two wages cheques to new employees not yet on the computer payroll and a subscription to a professional organisation. You are to arrange these payments on the documents shown on the next page (you do not need to write out any cheques, or to sign the standing order). The details are as follows:

(a) Wages of £89.00 to R Power at Western Bank, Broadfield, Code 33 76 54, account number 71976234.

(b) Wages of £155.00 to R Patel at Central Bank, Broadfield, Code 88 76 51, account number 04892192.

(c) Monthly subscription of £15.00 (starting 1 April 1998, until further notice) to Association of Software Designers at Eastern Bank, Mereford, 44 77 06, account number 21903461, reference 121092.

Date _____ | Date _____ | **bank giro credit** | £50 notes
Credit _____ | Cashier's stamp and | | £20 notes
 | initials | **Code no** | £10 notes
£50 notes | | **Bank** _____ | £5 notes
£20 notes | | **Branch** _____ | £1
£10 notes | | | 50p
£5 notes | | | 20p
£1 | **Credit** _____ | | 10p,5p
50p | **Account No.** _____ | | Bronze
20p | | | Total Cash
10p,5p | | | Cheques etc
Bronze | **Number of cheques** | **Paid in by** _____ |
Total Cash | | |
Cheques etc | | **Do not write below this line** |
£ | | | £

Date _____ | Date _____ | **bank giro credit** | £50 notes
Credit _____ | Cashier's stamp and | | £20 notes
 | initials | **Code no** | £10 notes
£50 notes | | **Bank** _____ | £5 notes
£20 notes | | **Branch** _____ | £1
£10 notes | | | 50p
£5 notes | | | 20p
£1 | **Credit** _____ | | 10p,5p
50p | **Account No.** _____ | | Bronze
20p | | | Total Cash
10p,5p | | | Cheques etc
Bronze | **Number of cheques** | **Paid in by** _____ |
Total Cash | | |
Cheques etc | | **Do not write below this line** |
£ | | | £

STANDING ORDER MANDATE

To _____ Bank

Address _____

PLEASE PAY TO

Bank _____ Branch _____ Sort code [   ]

Beneficiary _____ Account number [   ]

The sum of £ [   ] Amount in words _____

Date of first payment _____ Frequency of payment _____

Until _____ Reference _____

Account to be debited [   ] Account number [   ]

SIGNATURE(S) ....

.... date.......................

Note: photocopiable accounts and cash books are printed in the Appendix (see page 243).

15 CASH BOOK

NVQ coverage

unit 1   element 4

- *make entries in the cash book*
- *make entries in the ledger accounts*

15.1 Walter Harrison is a sole trader who records his cash and bank transactions in a three-column cash book. The following are the transactions for June 1997:

1 June	Balances: cash £280; bank overdraft £2,240
3 June	Received a cheque from G Wheaton for £195, in full settlement of a debt of £200
5 June	Received cash of £53 from T Francis, in full settlement of a debt of £55
9 June	Paid F Lloyd a cheque for £390 in full settlement of a debt of £400
10 June	Paid wages in cash £165
12 June	Paid A Morris in cash £97 in full settlement of a debt of £100
16 June	Withdrew £200 in cash from the bank for use in the business
18 June	Received a cheque for £640 from H Watson in full settlement of a debt of £670
20 June	Paid R Marks £78 by cheque
24 June	Paid D Farr £65 by cheque, in full settlement of a debt of £67
26 June	Paid telephone account £105 in cash
27 June	Received a cheque for £234 from M Perry in full settlement of a debt of £240
30 June	Received cash £45 from K Willis

All cheques are banked on the day of receipt.

You are to

- Enter the above transactions in Harrison's three-column cash book
- Balance the cash and bank columns at 30 June, and carry the balances down to 1 July.
- Total the two discount columns and show the discount accounts in the general ledger

15.2 You work as the cashier for Middleton Manufacturing Company. A work experience student from the local college is with you today. You show him the credit side of the cash book with last week's transactions as follows:

Cash Book (credit side only)

Date	Details	Folio	Discount received	Cash	Bank
1997			£	£	£
3 Nov	Balance b/d				687
3 Nov	Purchases			115	
4 Nov	H Hall Limited		15		585
5 Nov	Stationery			76	
5 Nov	Cash	C			795
6 Nov	Wages			795	
7 Nov	Office equipment				395
9 Nov	Balances c/d			115	1,561
			15	1,101	4,023

You are to explain to the student what each of the transactions represents and, where appropriate, the other accounting entry involved in the transaction. Ignore VAT.

15.3 Martin Peters runs a building supplies company. He buys in bulk from manufacturers and sells in smaller quantities to trade customers on credit and to the public on cash terms. His business is registered for VAT.

He uses a cash book which analyses *receipts* between:
- discount allowed
- VAT
- sales
- sales ledger
- sundry

Payments are analysed between:
- discount received
- VAT
- purchases
- purchases ledger
- sundry

The following transactions take place during the week commencing 17 November 1997 (all cheques are banked on the day of receipt):

17 Nov   Balances from previous week: cash £384.21, bank £1,576.80

17 Nov   Sales £354.25 (including VAT), cheques received

18 Nov   Sales £254.88 (including VAT), cash received

18 Nov   Paid an invoice for £292.65 from Wyvern Cement Company (a creditor) by cheque for £286.40 and receiving £6.25 discount for prompt settlement

19 Nov   Sales £476.29 (including VAT), cheques received

19 Nov   Paid for stationery in cash, £45.50 (including VAT)

20 Nov   Sales £351.48 (including VAT), cash received

20 Nov   Withdrew £200 cash from the bank for use in the business

20 Nov   Paid wages £782.31 in cash

21 Nov   A debtor, J Johnson, settles an invoice for £398.01, paying £389.51 by cheque, £8.50 discount being allowed for prompt settlement

21 Nov   Sales £487.29 (including VAT), cheques received

21 Nov   Paid an invoice for £468.25 from Broughton Brick Company (a creditor) by cheque for £458.25 and receiving £10.00 discount for prompt settlement

21 Nov   A debtor, Wyvern Council settles an invoice for £269.24 by cheque

You are to:

• Enter the above transactions in the analysed cash book of Martin Peters (VAT amounts should be rounded down to the nearest penny)

• Balance the cash book at 21 November 1997

NVQ coverage

unit 1 element 3

- *make entries in petty cash book*
- *analyse, total and post entries*

16 PETTY CASH BOOK

Note: photocopiable accounts and a petty cash
book are printed in the Appendix (see page 243).

16.1   A company operates its petty cash book using the imprest system. The imprest amount is £250.00. At the end of a particular period the analysis columns are totalled to give the following amounts:

VAT £13.42; postages £29.18; travel £45.47; stationery £33.29; sundry £18.54

How much cash will be required to restore the imprest amount for the next period?

16.2   You work as an accounts assistant in the offices of Hi-Tech Engineering Company, a VAT-registered business. One of your responsibilities is to maintain the petty cash records and you are authorised to approve petty cash vouchers up to a value of £15 each. How will you deal with the following discrepancies and queries?

- A petty cash voucher for stationery is submitted to you for £12.50; the till receipt from the stationery shop shows a total of £10.00

- A petty cash voucher for travelling expenses is submitted to you for £25.50; a rail ticket for this value is attached.

- The total of the analysis columns of the petty cash book is different from the total payments column.

- There is a difference between the balance shown in the petty cash book and the cash in the petty cash box.

- A colleague asks about the imprest amount and where you keep the keys to the petty cash box.

16.3   You are working in the accounts department of Deansway Trading, a VAT-registered company. One of your responsibilities is to maintain the petty cash records under the supervision of the office manager. The petty cash book is kept on the imprest system, with an imprest amount of £100. The petty cash book is balanced at the end of each week, and the imprest amount is restored to £100.

You are to:

- Prepare a suitable layout for recording petty cash transactions, with analysis columns for VAT, postages, travel, meals, and stationery (see Appendix 1 for an example).

- Using the information on the attached petty cash vouchers, which have been checked against receipts and authorised by the office manager, enter the relevant details for:
  - the week commencing 5 May 1997 (vouchers numbered 455-460)
  - the week commencing 12 May 1997 (vouchers numbered 461-472)
  Note that some payments are not subject to VAT and the office manager has marked these; all other payments include VAT.

- For each week, show how the following will be recorded in the double-entry book-keeping system:
  - the totals of the analysis columns
  - the transfers of cash from the main cashier

Vouchers for the week beginning 5 May 1997

PETTY CASH VOUCHER	No 455

Date   *5 May 1997*

	£	p
Postages	7	00
no VAT		
	7	00

Signature   *J Jones*   Authorised   *S Smith*

PETTY CASH VOUCHER	No 456

Date   *5 May 1997*

	£	p
Travel	2	85
no VAT		
	2	85

Signature   *J Jones*   Authorised   *S Smith*

PETTY CASH VOUCHER	No 457

Date   *6 May 1997*

	£	p
Meal allowance	6	11
no VAT		
	6	11

Signature   *R Singh*   Authorised   *S Smith*

PETTY CASH VOUCHER	No 458

Date   *7 May 1997*

	£	p
Taxi fare	4	70
	4	70

Signature   *J Jones*   Authorised   *S Smith*

PETTY CASH VOUCHER	No 459

Date   *8 May 1997*

	£	p
Stationery	3	76
	3	76

Signature   *J Jones*   Authorised   *S Smith*

PETTY CASH VOUCHER	No 460

Date   *9 May 1997*

	£	p
Postages	5	25
no VAT		
	5	25

Signature   *M Gono*   Authorised   *S Smith*

Vouchers for the week beginning 12 May 1997 (continued on the next page)

PETTY CASH VOUCHER		No 461
Date 12 May 1997	£	p
Travel	6	50
no VAT		
	6	50
Signature J Jones Authorised S Smith		

PETTY CASH VOUCHER		No 462
Date 13 May 1997	£	p
Meal allowance	6	11
no VAT		
	6	11
Signature J Jones Authorised S Smith		

PETTY CASH VOUCHER		No 463
Date 13 May 1997	£	p
Stationery	8	46
	8	46
Signature R Singh Authorised S Smith		

PETTY CASH VOUCHER		No 464
Date 13 May 1997	£	p
Taxi	5	17
	5	17
Signature J Jones Authorised S Smith		

PETTY CASH VOUCHER		No 465
Date 14 May 1997	£	p
Stationery	4	70
	4	70
Signature J Jones Authorised S Smith		

PETTY CASH VOUCHER		No 466
Date 14 May 1997	£	p
Travel	3	50
no VAT		
	3	50
Signature M Gono Authorised S Smith		

Vouchers for the week beginning 12 May 1997 (continued)

PETTY CASH VOUCHER	No 467

Date _14 May 1997_

	£	p
Postages	4	50
no VAT		
	4	50

Signature _J Jones_ Authorised _S Smith_

PETTY CASH VOUCHER	No 468

Date _15 May 1997_

	£	p
Bus fares	3	80
no VAT		
	3	80

Signature _J Jones_ Authorised _S Smith_

PETTY CASH VOUCHER	No 469

Date _15 May 1997_

	£	p
Catering expenses	10	81
	10	81

Signature _R Singh_ Authorised _S Smith_

PETTY CASH VOUCHER	No 470

Date _16 May 1997_

	£	p
Postages	3	50
no VAT		
	3	50

Signature _J Jones_ Authorised _S Smith_

PETTY CASH VOUCHER	No 471

Date _16 May 1997_

	£	p
Stationery	7	52
	7	52

Signature _J Jones_ Authorised _S Smith_

PETTY CASH VOUCHER	No 472

Date _16 May 1997_

	£	p
Travel expenses	6	45
no VAT		
	6	45

Signature _M Gono_ Authorised _S Smith_

NVQ coverage

unit 1 element 4

• preparing bank reconciliation statements

• dealing with discrepancies

17 BANK RECONCILIATION STATEMENTS

Note: a photocopiable three column cash book is printed in the Appendix (see page 243).

17.1 In preparing a bank reconciliation statement to agree the bank statement balance with the balance of the cash book:

(a) Would an unpresented cheque be added to or subtracted from the bank statement balance?

(b) Would an outstanding lodgement (ie an amount paid into the bank, but not yet recorded on the bank statement) be added to or subtracted from the bank statement balance?

17.2 Wyvern Wholesalers requires the bank statement and cash book balances (bank columns) to be reconciled. You are given the following information as at 30 April 1997:

• the bank columns of the cash book show a balance of £900 in the bank

• cheques for £120, £150 and £40 have been sent out in payment to various suppliers but have not yet been paid into the bank by those suppliers; they are recorded in the cash book

• a direct debit payment of £45 has been recorded by the bank, but has not yet been entered in the cash book

• a cheque for £500 has been recorded as a receipt in the cash book, and paid into the bank; it has not yet been credited by the bank

• bank charges amounting to £20 appear on the bank statement, but have not yet been entered in the cash book

• a bank giro credit from a customer for £150 appears on the bank statement, but has not yet been entered in the cash book

• the bank statement shows a closing bank balance of £795 Cr

You are to:

(a) write the cash book up-to-date at 30 April 1997

(b) prepare a bank reconciliation statement at 30 April 1997

17.3 You work as a trainee in the office of Speciality Paints Limited, a company which buys special types of paints and other finishes from the manufacturers and sells them in your area to local businesses. This week the cashier, who is responsible for keeping the company's cash book is away on holiday. You have been asked to carry out her work for the week commencing 8 September 1997.

At the start of the week the cash book has a balance at bank of £802.50, and cash in hand of £120.68. The following are the transactions to be entered in the cash book for the week:

Cheques received from debtors

8 Sep   £389.51 from Wyvern County Council, in full settlement of an invoice for £398.01

10 Sep   £451.20 from J Jones & Company

12 Sep   £458.25 from Building Supplies Limited, in full settlement of an invoice for £468.25

Note: all cheques received are banked on the day of receipt.

Cheques drawn

8 Sep   Cheque no. 123451 for £263.49, payee ITI Paint Division Limited, a creditor, in full settlement of an invoice for £269.24

9 Sep   Cheque no. 123452 for £100.00, payee Cash (the cash was drawn for use in the business)

9 Sep   Cheque no. 123453 for £169.75, payee United Telecom plc

10 Sep   Cheque no. 123454 for £394.20, payee Wages

11 Sep   Cheque no. 123455 for £160.38, payee Paint Manufacturing plc, in full settlement of an invoice for £163.88

Cash received from debtors

9 Sep   £27.50 from T Lewis

12 Sep   £22.91 from H Simms, in full settlement of an invoice for £23.41

Cash paid

11 Sep   £88.50 for casual labour

At the end of the week, the bank statement shown on the next page is received.

You are to:

*   Enter the transactions for the week in the three-column cash book of Speciality Paints Limited.

*   Using the bank statement, write the cash book (bank columns) up-to-date with any items appearing on the bank statement that need to be recorded in the cash book.

*   Balance the cash book at 12 September 1997, and show the discount accounts as they will appear in the firm's general ledger.

*   Prepare bank reconciliation statements at:

    –   8 September 1997 (in order to agree the opening bank statement and cash book balances)

    –   12 September 1997

*   Write a memorandum to the office manager regarding any matter that you consider should be queried with the bank. Use a photocopy of the blank memorandum printed on page 84. Do not write on the original page – you may need it later.

National Bank PLC

Branch Mereford

Account   Speciality Paints Ltd

Account number 12345678   **Statement number** 45   **date** 12 Sep 1997

Date	Details	Withdrawals	Deposits	Balance
1997		£	£	£
8 Sep	Balance brought forward			967.00 Cr
8 Sep	Credit		389.51	1,356.51 Cr
9 Sep	Cheque 123450	164.50		1,192.01 Cr
9 Sep	Cheque 123452	100.00		1,092.01 Cr
9 Sep	DD Wyvern Hire Purchase	85.50		1,006.51 Cr
10 Sep	Cheque 123454	394.20		612.31 Cr
10 Sep	Credit		451.20	1,063.51 Cr
10 Sep	BGC Johnson & Co		125.50	1,189.01 Cr
11 Sep	Cheque 123451	263.49		925.52 Cr
11 Sep	Cheque 874111	25.00		900.52 Cr
12 Sep	Bank charges	12.50		888.02 Cr

SO Standing Order **DD** Direct Debit   **TR** Transfer   **BGC** Bank giro credit   **BACS** Automated transfer

Why do we not enter 164.50 in Cash Book when updating

MEMORANDUM

To

From

Date

Subject

Section 2
devolved assessment tasks

DEVOLVED ASSESSMENT TASKS – DAVIES CASH AND CARRY

The table below lists the performance criteria that are covered by the tasks. The relevant tasks are listed in the right-hand column.

UNIT 1: RECORDING AND ACCOUNTING FOR CASH TRANSACTIONS

element 1

record and bank monies received	task
❏ monies are banked in accordance with organisation's policies, regulations, procedures and timescales	1.2
❏ incoming monies are checked against relevant supporting documentation	1.1
❏ cash is correctly counted and correct change given where applicable	1.1
❏ monies received are correctly and legibly recorded	1.1
❏ totals and balances are correctly calculated	1.1
❏ paying in documents are correctly prepared and reconciled to relevant records	1.2
❏ discrepancies, unusual features or queries are identified and either resolved or referred to the appropriate person	1.3

element 2

make and record payments

❏ payments are made and recorded in accordance with the organisation's policies, regulations, procedures and timescales	4.1,4.2
❏ payments are properly authorised	4.1
❏ cheques are prepared correctly and are signed by designated person(s) prior to despatch	4.1
❏ standing orders and other inter-bank transfers are correctly documented	3.2
❏ remittance advices are correctly prepared and despatched with payments	4.3
❏ available cash discounts are identified and deducted	4.1

element 3

maintain petty cash records	task
❏ *transactions are accurately recorded and analysed to the correct expenditure heads*	*2.4*
❏ *cash withdrawals from the main cash account are accurately recorded*	*2.4*
❏ *claims are properly authorised, are within prescribed limits and are supported by adequate evidence*	*2.3,2.1*
❏ *totals and balances are correctly calculated*	*2.4*
❏ *analysed totals of petty cash expenditure are transferred to the correct ledger accounts*	*2.5*
❏ *any discrepancies, unusual features or queries are identified and either resolved or referred to the appropriate person*	*2.3*

element 4

account for cash and bank transactions	task
❏ *entries in the cash book are accurately transferred to correct ledger accounts*	*1.4*
❏ *bank reconciliation statements are accurately prepared and are presented within specified timescales*	*3.1*
❏ *recorded transactions are supported by properly authorised primary documentation*	*3.2*
❏ *details for the relevant primary documentation are recorded in the cash book and analysed accurately*	*4.2*
❏ *totals and balances are correctly calculated*	*3.1*
❏ *the organisation's policies, regulations, procedures and timescales are observed*	*3.1,3.2,3.3*
❏ *any discrepancies, unusual features or queries are identified and either resolved or referred to the appropriate person*	*3.3*

INTRODUCTION

You work as the Accounts Clerk of Bernard Davies & Sons Limited, a small wholesale cash and carry business located at 701 Faulkner Street, Manchester M4 8DY. Your duties include checking cash received at the tills, paying monies received into the bank, preparing bank reconciliation statements and sending out cheques to suppliers. You are also responsible for maintaining the petty cash system.

Today is Friday 5 September 1997. You will need to carry out a variety of tasks in accordance with the firm's procedures which are described below.

CASH AND CARRY SALES

There are two tills in operation in the warehouse. Customers can pay at either till - in the form of cash, debit or credit card, or with a business cheque (provided they have previously been authorised to do so; such authorisation will be noted on the customer's buying card).

The till rolls are in duplicate. When a sale is made, the Till Operator keys in the appropriate details (including the name of the customer and the method of payment, cash, cards, or cheque), detaches the top copy and gives it to the customer as a receipt. The bottom copy remains on the roll. Completed till rolls are retained for internal control purposes.

At the end of the day, each Till Operator prepares a sales summary sheet, by reference to the till roll. The Till Supervisor then empties the tills and passes the sales summary sheets, together with the notes, coins and cheques, to you.

One of your responsibilities is to reconcile the cash received to the sales summaries for each till before depositing the cash into the night safe at the bank. After completing the reconciliations you are required to fill in a confirmation of sales slip for each till. This slip is to be returned to the Till Supervisor. The slip contains space for an explanation of any discrepancies found. In the event that a discrepancy prevents a reconciliation altogether, the confirmation slip must not be signed and appropriate investigation must be made. If the cause of the discrepancy is apparent, an appropriate explanation must be given, but the slip may be signed as usual. Whether or not there is a discrepancy, all cash received must be banked in the night safe as a precaution against theft.

BANK RECONCILIATION

The bank reconciliation statement must be prepared each month. If it is discovered that cheques sent out more than a month ago have yet to clear on the bank statement they must be notified to the Accountant, Mr Seymour.

PETTY CASH

You have just been placed in charge of the petty cash system, following the departure of the person previously responsible. The petty cash is operated on the imprest system, with an imprest amount of £200. All claimants must complete a petty cash voucher and provide a receipt for expenditure incurred. You are able to authorise expenditure up to £50 - the maximum claim payable out of petty cash. You are also required to enter the vouchers in numerical order into an analysed petty cash book.

ACCOUNTING RECORDS

All cash received is recorded in a receipts cash book, showing the appropriate bank paying-in slip number. All payments are recorded in a separate payments cash book.

FURTHER INFORMATION

The company is registered for VAT and charges VAT at the rate of 17.5% on all sales.

The company's suppliers offer cash discounts, at varying rates, for early settlement of accounts.

The personnel involved in this simulation are as follows:

Accounts Clerk	Yourself
Accountant	Mr Seymour
Till Supervisor	Joanne Derbyshire
Till Operators	Susan Kenny and Liz Smith
Sales Representatives	Deirdre Smith and Arthur Duncan

Extracts of list of customer addresses:

Alan Lawlor
19 Giggs Drive
Manchester M17 4QP

Hammerson & Co
Salport Industrial Estate
Manchester M5 1OR

Martin & Priestley Ltd
64 Alandale Way
Manchester M13 8YY

Peter Smith Ltd
Brondby Lane
Manchester M4 6YZ

James Grimes
The Holly Trees
Arndale Road
Manchester M14 1PX

W. Williamson
19 Lavender Road
Manchester M26 2AX

PART ONE

Customers pay for their goods at either of the two tills available. Till 1 is operated by Susan Kenny and Till 2 is operated by Liz Smith. Both Till Operators can take money in the form of cash, debit or credit card, or in the form of a cheque provided the customer has authorisation to pay by cheque.

One of your duties at the end of each day is to pay all monies received during the day into the bank night safe. This will include the day's takings plus any cheques received in the post from credit customers. The day's takings are brought to you by the Till Supervisor, Joanne Derbyshire, together with the sales summary sheets prepared by the Till Operators. Before you pay the takings into the bank you must reconcile the amounts taken at each till with the amounts shown on the sales summary sheets for eachTill Operator and sign a confirmation slip to that effect.

Joanne Derbyshire therefore gives you two separate bags of money (one for each till) in order for you to identify on which till any shortages may occur.

On Friday 5 September 1997, she presents you with the following:

Bag One (from Till 1, Susan Kenny):		Bag Two (from Till 2, Liz Smith):	
£50	10	£50	2
£20	20	£20	11
£10	29	£10	19
£5	5	£5	2
£1	27	£1	14
50p	9	50p	3
20p	9	20p	8
10p	7	10p	6
5p	5	5p	1
2p	11	2p	3
1p	7	1p	1

In addition, there were two cheques:

T Denton - £92.10

S Tench - £174.29

There were also two cheques:

P Anderson - £96.47

R Elliott - £124.70

PART ONE – TASKS

1.1 Reconcile the amounts presented to you in each bag by Joanne Derbyshire with the totals shown on the sales summary sheets. Then complete the confirmation of sales slips on the next page. Note: keep your workings – your tutor may want to see them.

SALES SUMMARY SHEET

Till no *1* Date *5/9/97*

Customer name	Amount (£)	Cash	Cheque	Credit/debit Card
R Ashton	86.70	✔		
F Trueman	63.22	✔		
R Charlton	121.90	✔		
T Endercott	64.13	✔		
T Denton	92.10		✔	
E Bloor	84.16	✔		
A Lucas	117.32	✔		
R Agnew	82.01	✔		
D Crawley	43.75	✔		
B Shaw	25.60	✔		
G Lloyd	132.17	✔		
S Tench	174.29		✔	
H Brown	201.64	✔		
E Taylor	52.28	✔		
R Patel	174.66	✔		

SALES SUMMARY SHEET

Till no 2 Date *5/9/97*

Customer name	Amount (£)	Cash	Cheque	Credit/debit Card
A Garner	71.30	✔		
P Anderson	96.47		✔	
L P Hartley	41.80	✔		
B White	75.60	✔		
I Roper	26.00			✔
R Elliott	124.70		✔	
B Norris	55.94	✔		
M Jarvis	126.97	✔		
R Parker	140.21	✔		

CONFIRMATION OF SALES SLIP

Till no................................Operator...Date.......................

      RECEIVED: CASH, CHEQUES,DEBIT/CREDIT CARDS   £.....................................

      TOTAL PER SALES SUMMARY   £.....................................

Discrepancies: ....

                ....

Signed   ....

CONFIRMATION OF SALES SLIP

Till no................................Operator...Date.......................

      RECEIVED: CASH, CHEQUES,DEBIT/CREDIT CARDS   £.....................................

      TOTAL PER SALES SUMMARY   £.....................................

Discrepancies: ....

                ....

Signed   ....

1.2 Complete both sides of the bank paying-in slip provided (see below) to record the day's banking on Friday 5 September 1997 which will include the day's takings from both tills as well as the cheques received from credit customers (see the next two pages). You should first ensure that the cheques received have been completed correctly.

Date _____	**bank giro credit**			£50 notes		
Cashier's stamp and initials				£20 notes		
	Code 10 -18 -35			£10 notes		
	NORTH WEST BANK PLC			£5 notes		
	Moston Branch			£1		
				50p		
	Bernard Davies & Sons Ltd			20p		
Credit				10p,5p		
Account No.	68473841			Bronze		
				Total Cash		
Number of cheques	Paid in by _____			Cheques etc		
	Do not write below this line			**£**		

No. 2735

Details of cheques etc		Amount
TOTAL CARRIED OVER **£**		

1.3   Where a cheque has been completed incorrectly, you should return it to the customer so that a replacement can be issued. Use the letterheads on the pages that follow the cheques to write to the customer(s) concerned.

The cheques from credit customers are shown below.

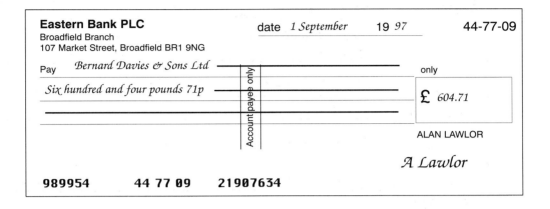

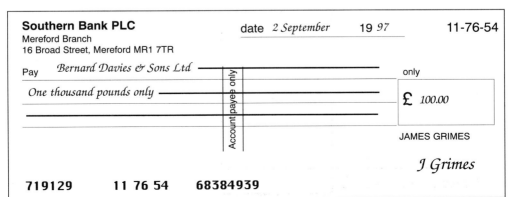

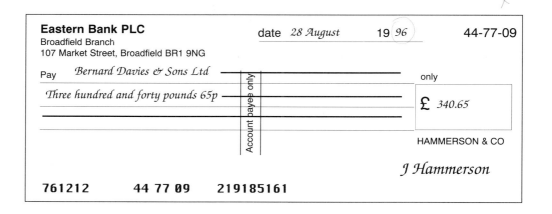

Eastern Bank PLC
Broadfield Branch
107 Market Street, Broadfield BR1 9NG

date *28 August* 19 96   44-77-09

Pay   *Bernard Davies & Sons Ltd*   only

Three hundred and forty pounds 65p

£ *340.65*

HAMMERSON & CO

J Hammerson

761212   44 77 09   219185161

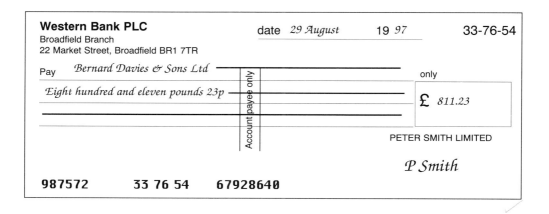

Western Bank PLC
Broadfield Branch
22 Market Street, Broadfield BR1 7TR

date *29 August* 19 97   33-76-54

Pay   *Bernard Davies & Sons Ltd*   only

Eight hundred and eleven pounds 23p

£ *811.23*

PETER SMITH LIMITED

P Smith

987572   33 76 54   67928640

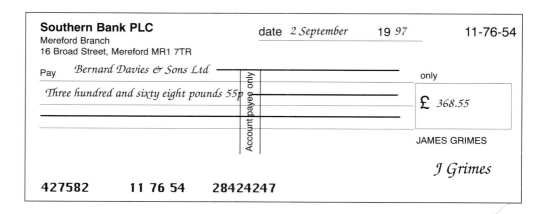

Southern Bank PLC
Mereford Branch
16 Broad Street, Mereford MR1 7TR

date *2 September* 19 97   11-76-54

Pay   *Bernard Davies & Sons Ltd*   only

Three hundred and sixty eight pounds 55p

£ *368.55*

JAMES GRIMES

J Grimes

427582   11 76 54   28424247

Bernard Davies & Sons Limited
701 Faulkner Street
Manchester
M4 8DY
Tel 0161 428 2051 Fax 0161 428 2053

Bernard Davies & Sons Limited. Registered Office 701 Faulkner Street Manchester M4 8DY
Registered in England 2654379 VAT Reg GB 929384746

Bernard Davies & Sons Limited

701 Faulkner Street
Manchester
M4 8DY
Tel 0161 428 2051 Fax 0161 428 2053

1.4   Provided that the cheques received from credit customers have been completed correctly, enter them in the appropriate sales ledger accounts shown on the next two pages.

Dr   **Alan Lawlor**   Cr

Date	Details	Amount	Date	Details	Amount
1997 Sep 1	Balance b/d	£ 604.71	1997		£

Dr   **Martin & Priestley Limited**   Cr

Date	Details	Amount	Date	Details	Amount
1997 Sep 1	Balance b/d	£ 2,360.90	1997		£

Dr   **J Grimes**   Cr

Date	Details	Amount	Date	Details	Amount
1997 Sep 1	Balance b/d	£ 1,275.30	1997		£

Dr   **Hammerson & Co**   Cr

Date	Details	Amount	Date	Details	Amount
1997 Sep 1	Balance b/d	£ 593.60	1997		£

Dr   **Peter Smith Limited**   Cr

Date	Details	Amount	Date	Details	Amount
1997 Sep 1	Balance b/d	£ 1,237.45	1997		£

Dr   **W Williamson**   Cr

Date	Details	Amount	Date	Details	Amount
1997 Sep 1	Balance b/d	£ 368.55	1997		£

PART TWO

The Accountant, Mr Seymour, has sent you a memorandum which informs you about those expenses that can be reimbursed and those expenses which will include VAT. He has also suggested in the memorandum that it would be a good idea for you to send a memorandum to all staff in order to remind them:

1.   How the petty cash system works.

2.   How much staff can claim.

3.   The need for staff to obtain receipts to support their claims.

Mr Seymour's memorandum included the following text:

APPROVED EXPENSES THAT CAN BE REIMBURSED

Petrol or diesel fuel (this can only be claimed by sales representatives)

Stationery

Casual wages

Window cleaning (to be analysed as office expenses)

Travelling expenses

Stamps and postage

Tea, coffee etc (to be analysed as office expenses).

EXPENSES ON WHICH VAT IS PAYABLE (provided the supplier is VAT registered)

Petrol or diesel fuel

Stationery

Window cleaning

Taxi fares

PART TWO – TASKS

2.1   Write the memorandum to all staff suggested by Mr Seymour. Use the form on the next page.

2.2   The procedures manual states that the imprest amount shall be £200. Mr Seymour has given you the amount of cash necessary to top up the existing balance of petty cash to the imprest amount. You are therefore required to enter this into the Petty Cash Book provided on page 101.

2.3   On your first day in charge of the petty cash system you have been presented with ten claims. These are reproduced, along with supporting receipts where available, on pages 102 - 105.

You are required to authorise those claims which you feel are valid and which can be reimbursed out of petty cash. You must sign in your own name the 'authorised' element of the the appropriate petty cash vouchers.

2.4   All the vouchers which you have authorised must be entered in the Petty Cash Book provided on page 101. The analysis columns must be completed and totalled as at close of business today, Friday 5 September 1997. The Petty Cash Book must be balanced and you must show the entries to restore the imprest.

2.5   You are required to complete the double entry by posting the totals of the analysis columns to the appropriate accounts in the General Ledger provided on pages 106 to 107.

MEMORANDUM

To

From

Date

Subject

PETTY CASH BOOK

Receipts	Date	Details	Voucher No.	Payment							
					VAT	Postage	Stationery	Office Expenses	Petrol/ diesel	Travel Expenses	
											Analysis columns
£				£	£	£	£	£	£	£	
76.32	1997 4 Sep	Balance b/f									

PETTY CASH VOUCHER		No *800*
Date *5 September 1997*		
	£	p
Computer disks	107	86
	107	86
Signature *R Singh* Authorised		

PETTY CASH VOUCHER		No *801*
Date *5 September 1997*		
	£	p
Stamps	9	50
	9	50
Signature *J Jones* Authorised		

PETTY CASH VOUCHER		No *802*
Date *5 September 1997*		
	£	p
Petrol	20	00
	20	00
Signature *R Singh* Authorised		

PETTY CASH VOUCHER		No *803*
Date *5 September 1997*		
	£	p
Taxi fare	3	85
	3	85
Signature *P Smith* Authorised		

PETTY CASH VOUCHER		No *804*
Date *5 September 1997*		
	£	p
Postage on parcel	6	20
	6	20
Signature *R Patel* Authorised		

PETTY CASH VOUCHER		No *805*
Date *5 September 1997*		
	£	p
Instant coffee	5	60
	5	60
Signature *M Gini* Authorised		

PETTY CASH VOUCHER		No *806*
Date *5 September 1997*		
	£	p
Petrol	28	00
	28	00
Signature *J Jones* Authorised		

PETTY CASH VOUCHER		No *807*
Date *5 September 1997*		
	£	p
Envelopes	11	25
	11	25
Signature *J Jones* Authorised		

PETTY CASH VOUCHER		No *808*
Date *5 September 1997*		
	£	p
Window cleaning	8	00
	8	00
Signature *R Singh* Authorised		

PETTY CASH VOUCHER		No *809*
Date *5 September 1997*		
	£	p
Taxi fare	11	28
	11	28
Signature *J Jones* Authorised		

supporting documents . . .

───────────────── **INVOICE** ─────────────────
COMPUTER SUPPLIES LIMITED
16 HARLEY WAY MANCHESTER M3 6BY
Tel 0161 429 5314 Fax 0161 429 5951 Email toni@cool.u-net.com
VAT Reg GB 0745 4672 71

invoice to

invoice no	2714
account	3993
your reference	47609
date/tax point	05 09 97

Bernard Davies & Sons Ltd
701 Faulkner Street
Manchester
M4 8DY

product code	description	quantity	price	unit	total	discount %	net
244	Zipo computer disks HD, PC formatted	18	5.10	box	91.80	0.00	91.80

goods total	91.80
VAT	16.06
TOTAL	107.86

terms
Payable on delivery

POST OFFICE	Receipt
Stamps	*£9.50*
TOTAL	*£9.50*

HYLTON FUEL
Hylton Road, Worcester WR2 5GN
VAT Reg 229 7543 26

31 litres unleaded	20.00
Cash tendered	20.00

04.09.97 14.23

POST OFFICE	Receipt
Parcel postage	*£6.20*
TOTAL	*£6.20*

Star Stationery
Deansgate, Manchester M1 3RT
VAT Reg 333 7804 01

05.09.97 09.30

200 envelopes C4	11.25
Total	11.25
Cash tendered	12.00
Change	00.75

Maxi Minicabs
Enstone Road, Gatley SK8 4JL

RECEIVED   **£**   *3.85*

VAT Reg 229 7543 26

Taxi to work when car would not start.

VALUE FOODSTORE
23 JOHN STREET WYTHENSHAWE

Tea	2.70
Coffee	2.90
Total	5.60
Cash tendered	10.00
Change	4.40

05.09.97 10.30

Phil Johns, Windowcleaning
23 Garden Road, Sale, M9 4GF

RECEIVED   **£**   *8.00*

Phil Johns is not registered for VAT

Maxi Minicabs
Enstone Road, Gatley SK8 4JL

RECEIVED   **£**   *11.28*

VAT Reg 229 7543 26

Taxi to railway station for business trip.

Dr   **VAT Account**   Cr

Date	Details	Amount	Date	Details	Amount
1997		£	1997		£

Dr   **Postages Account**   Cr

Date	Details	Amount	Date	Details	Amount
1997		£	1997		£

Dr   **Stationery Account**   Cr

Date	Details	Amount	Date	Details	Amount
1997		£	1997		£

Dr   **Office Expenses Account**   Cr

Date	Details	Amount	Date	Details	Amount
1997		£	1997		£

Dr   **Petrol/diesel Account**   Cr

Date	Details	Amount	Date	Details	Amount
1997		£	1997		£

Dr   **Travel Expenses Account**   Cr

Date	Details	Amount	Date	Details	Amount
1997		£	1997		£

PART THREE

Each month a bank reconciliation statement is prepared in order to reconcile the balance on the monthly bank statement sent by the bank with the cash book balance, and to identify any cheques issued that have not been cleared by the bank.

PART THREE – TASKS

3.1   The Accountant asks you to prepare the bank reconciliation statement for the month of August 1997. Therefore you are required to update the receipts and payments cash books from the details on the bank statement and, having ascertained the new totals, calculate the closing cash book balance and prepare the bank reconciliation statement. (Use page 114 for this purpose).

The previous month's bank reconciliation was:

	£
Balance as per bank statement no. 81	22,496.40
less unpresented cheques: (see schedule)	6,504.24
Balance as per cash book	15,992.16

The schedule of unpresented cheques was:

Date	Cheque No.	Payee	Amount
			£
14/7/97	090792	J B McKay Ltd	248.30
15/7/97	090816	M Moore	92.60
21/7/97	090824	L Davidson	148.22
21/7/97	090840	C Openshaw Ltd	2,046.90
29/7/97	090846	Brian Cockcroft	709.00
29/7/97	090847	Berry & Wilkinson	843.80
29/7/97	090848	Derek White & Co Ltd	1,206.36
29/7/97	090849	Harper & Law Ltd	775.00
29/7/97	090850	T & J Preston Ltd	22.96
29/7/97	090851	Manchester Supply Company	411.10

This month's bank statements and the relevant pages of the receipts and payments cash books appear on the pages that follow.

NORTHWEST BANK PLC

620 Lower High Street
Moston
Manchester

Statement of Account

Account: Bernard Davies & Sons Ltd
Account no 68473841   Statement no 82   Statement date 29 Aug 1997

Date	Details	Withdrawals	Deposits	Balance
1997		£	£	£
30 Jul	Balance brought forward			22,496.40 Cr
4 Aug	090792	248.30		
4 Aug	090824	148.22		
4 Aug	BGC M Armson		471.30	22,571.18 Cr
5 Aug	090816	92.60		
5 Aug	SO Commercial Insurance	87.62		
5 Aug	Credit 2712		2,610.93	25,001.89 Cr
6 Aug	Credit 2713		708.40	25,710.29 Cr
7 Aug	090847	843.80		
7 Aug	090848	1,206.36		
7 Aug	090849	775.00		
7 Aug	Credit 2714		1,662.47	24,547.60 Cr
8 Aug	Credit 2715		346.13	24,893.73 Cr
11 Aug	090846	709.00		
11 Aug	090850	22.96		
11 Aug	090851	411.10		
11 Aug	090852	870.56		
11 Aug	DD Courier Services Plc	410.00		
11 Aug	Credit 2716		3,864.27	
11 Aug	Balance carried forward			26,334.38 Cr

SO Standing Order **DD** Direct Debit **TR** Transfer **BGC** Bank giro credit **BACS** Automated transfer

NORTHWEST BANK PLC			**Statement of Account**	
620 Lower High Street				
Moston				
Manchester				

Account: Bernard Davies & Sons Ltd
Account no 68473841   **Statement no** 83   **Statement date** 29 Aug 1997

Date	Details	Withdrawals	Deposits	Balance
1997		£	£	£
12 Aug	Balance brought forward			26,334.38 Cr
12 Aug	090854	664.72		
12 Aug	Credit 2717		492.00	26,161.66 Cr
13 Aug	090853	1,260.00		
13 Aug	090855	907.20		
13 Aug	090856	246.80		
13 Aug	Credit 2718		744.09	24,491.75 Cr
14 Aug	Credit 2719		1,173.14	25,664.89 Cr
15 Aug	BGC W Farrell Plc		710.00	
15 Aug	Credit 2720		487.26	26,862.15 Cr
18 Aug	Credit 2721		2,734.61	29,596.76 Cr
19 Aug	090857	694.14		
19 Aug	090859	311.18		
19 Aug	090860	690.00		
19 Aug	090861	1,362.40		
19 Aug	Credit 2722		977.02	27,516.06 Cr
20 Aug	SO Equipment Leasing PLC	3,200.00		
20 Aug	Credit 2723		208.00	
20 Aug	Balance carried forward			24,524.06 Cr

SO Standing Order **DD** Direct Debit **TR** Transfer **BGC** Bank giro credit **BACS** Automated transfer

NORTHWEST BANK PLC

620 Lower High Street
Moston
Manchester M22 8RJ

Statement of Account

Account: Bernard Davies & Sons Ltd
Account no 68473841   Statement no 84   Statement date 29 Aug 1997

Date	Details	Withdrawals	Deposits	Balance
1997		£	£	£
21 Aug	Balance brought forward			24,524.06 Cr
21 Aug	090862	771.22		
21 Aug	Credit 2724		1,178.64	24,931.48 Cr
22 Aug	090864	3,062.70		
22 Aug	Credit 2725		600.28	22,469.06 Cr
25 Aug	090863	505.94		
25 Aug	090865	894.48		
25 Aug	090866	402.00		
25 Aug	DD Manchester Motors	200.00		
25 Aug	Credit 2726		3,089.64	23,556.28 Cr
26 Aug	Credit 2727		491.17	24,047.45 Cr
27 Aug	BGC Sweets Limited		592.10	
27 Aug	090867	276.60		
27 Aug	090869	1,417.36		
27 Aug	Credit 2728		886.50	23,832.09 Cr
28 Aug	090868	896.22		
28 Aug	090870	27.84		
28 Aug	090871	201.96		
28 Aug	090872	47.80		
28 Aug	090873	2,092.78		
28 Aug	Credit 2729		643.91	21,209.40 Cr
29 Aug	SO Training Services Ltd	170.00		
29 Aug	Credit 2730		505.77	
29 Aug	Balance carried forward			21,545.17 Cr

SO Standing Order **DD** Direct Debit **TR** Transfer **BGC** Bank giro credit **BACS** Automated transfer

CASH BOOK – RECEIPTS

Date	Details	Amount (£)
		Bal B/D *15,992.16*
5/8/97	Cash & cheques	2,610.93
6/8/97	Cash & cheques	708.40
7/8/97	Cash & cheques	1,662.47
8/8/97	Cash & cheques	346.13
11/8/97	Cash & cheques	3,864.27
12/8/97	Cash & cheques	492.00
13/8/97	Cash & cheques	744.09
14/8/97	Cash & cheques	1,173.14
15/8/97	Cash & cheques	487.26
18/8/97	Cash & cheques	2,734.61
19/8/97	Cash & cheques	977.02
20/8/97	Cash & cheques	208.00
21/8/97	Cash & cheques	1,178.64
22/8/97	Cash & cheques	600.28
25/8/97	Cash & cheques	3,089.64
26/8/97	Cash & cheques	491.17
27/8/97	Cash & cheques	886.50
28/8/97	Cash & cheques	643.91
29/8/97	Cash & cheques	505.77
		23,404.23
		39,396.39

Bal 12,432.39

CASH BOOK – PAYMENTS

Date	Cheque no.	Payee	Amount (£)
4/8/97	090852	Coleman Bros Ltd	870.56
4/8/97	090853	Benson & Shaw Ltd	1,260.00
4/8/97	090854	Preston, McKay Ltd	664.72
5/8/97	090855	G Watson	907.20
5/8/97	090856	P Pendlebury Ltd	246.80
11/8/97	090857	G C Lipton Ltd	694.14
11/8/97	090858	W Walker Ltd	512.62
11/8/97	090859	D Newton	311.18
11/8/97	090860	Moston Traders Ltd	690.00
11/8/97	090861	W & A Buckley	1,362.40
13/8/97	090862	B Donnelly	771.22
15/8/97	090863	Modern Clothng Company	505.94
15/8/97	090864	Smith Dawson & Roe	3,062.70
15/8/97	090865	Textile Supplies PLC	894.48
15/8/97	090866	Manchester Fashion Co	402.00
19/8/97	090867	Denis Weatherall	276.60
19/8/97	090868	A to Z Couriers Ltd	896.22
19/8/97	090869	Bowen & Stott Ltd	1,417.36
22/8/97	090870	T Morgan	27.84
22/8/97	090871	A McClair	201.96
22/8/97	090872	A Thorp	47.80
22/8/97	090873	Cooper & Roache PLC	2,092.78
26/8/97	090874	J M Bargains Ltd	1,771.96
26/8/97	090875	E Edwards	824.52
26/8/97	090876	D D Supplies	606.00
26/8/97	090877	Roberts Bros	1,130.70
27/8/97	090878	A Lawrence Ltd	448.25
27/8/97	090879	L Warriner PLC	672.11
27/8/97	090880	Murray & Trueman	912.22
27/8/97	090881	D Wallace & Co Ltd	307.64
27/8/97	090882	K Newell Ltd	192.80
27/8/97	090883	Charnley Motor Factors	278.00
27/8/97	090884	Northern Import Company	1,490.00
27/8/97	090885	B J KIng Ltd	213.28

26,964 00

CALCULATION OF CLOSING CASH BOOK BALANCE

£

Opening cash book balance   *15,992.16*

Add updated receipts cash book total   _____

Less updated payments cash book total   _____

Closing cash book balance   _____
                                                         _____

BANK RECONCILIATION STATEMENT

as at _____

3.2   In completing the cash book entries you will have noticed that not all items appearing on the bank statement had been entered in the cash book.

Explain, in general terms, the procedures you would take to satisfy yourself as to the validity of these items (both debit and credit). You are not required to give a detailed explanation of each entry; it is sufficient to give a general explanation, illustrating your answer by referring to one specific debit entry and one specific credit entry on the bank statement.

Write your answer in the space provided below.

3.3 The firm's procedures manual states that any cheques sent out to creditors but not presented to the bank after a period of one month has elapsed, must be reported to the Accountant, Mr Seymour, by the person preparing the bank reconciliation statement. You are therefore required to send the memorandum to Mr Seymour using the form provided below. Today's date is Friday 5 September 1997.

MEMORANDUM

To

From

Date

Subject

PART FOUR

The accountant, Mr Seymour, has informed you today, Friday 5 September 1997, that the following invoices can now be paid:

Supplier	Invoice Number	Invoice Date	Amount Goods £	VAT £	Terms	
Michael Anderton	0362	19/8/97	710.00	118.03	5%	14 days
Sudbury Basement Ltd	37102	12/8/97	960.00	163.80	2.5%	14 days
J S. Carter & Co	711	18/8/97	800.40	133.06	5%	30 days
Chisholm & Jones Ltd	265	1/9/97	604.84	100.55	5%	7 days
P & J Corrigan Ltd	1764	15/8/97	62.50	10.93	Net	30 days
G M Trading Co Ltd	503	27/8/97	211.90	36.15	2.5%	7 days
Northern Textile Company	0819	26/8/97	1,120.00	186.20	5%	14 days
Barry Smart Ltd	87	8/8/97	131.80	23.06	Net	30 days
Supersave Plc	9011	11/8/97	324.80	56.84	Net	30 days
Denis Watson Ltd	228	19/8/97	609.54	101.33	5%	14 days

PART FOUR – TASKS

Complete the cheques to be sent to each supplier ready for signature by a director. Ensure that the correct amount of cash discount is taken in each case, where it is applicable.

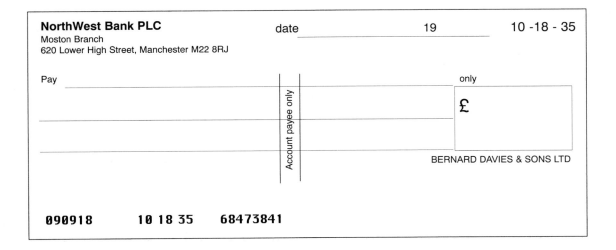

NorthWest Bank PLC
Moston Branch
620 Lower High Street, Manchester M22 8RJ

date _____ 19 _____   10 -18 - 35

Pay _____   only

Account payee only

£

BERNARD DAVIES & SONS LTD

090919   10 18 35   68473841

NorthWest Bank PLC
Moston Branch
620 Lower High Street, Manchester M22 8RJ

date _____ 19 _____   10 -18 - 35

Pay _____   only

Account payee only

£

BERNARD DAVIES & SONS LTD

090920   10 18 35   68473841

NorthWest Bank PLC
Moston Branch
620 Lower High Street, Manchester M22 8RJ

date _____ 19 _____   10 -18 - 35

Pay _____   only

Account payee only

£

BERNARD DAVIES & SONS LTD

090921   10 18 35   68473841

NorthWest Bank PLC
Moston Branch
620 Lower High Street, Manchester M22 8RJ

date _____ 19 _____   10 -18 - 35

Pay _____

Account payee only

only

£

BERNARD DAVIES & SONS LTD

090922   **10 18 35**   **68473841**

NorthWest Bank PLC
Moston Branch
620 Lower High Street, Manchester M22 8RJ

date _____ 19 _____   10 -18 - 35

Pay _____

Account payee only

only

£

BERNARD DAVIES & SONS LTD

090923   **10 18 35**   **68473841**

NorthWest Bank PLC
Moston Branch
620 Lower High Street, Manchester M22 8RJ

date _____ 19 _____   10 -18 - 35

Pay _____

Account payee only

only

£

BERNARD DAVIES & SONS LTD

090924   **10 18 35**   **68473841**

NorthWest Bank PLC
Moston Branch
620 Lower High Street, Manchester M22 8RJ

date _____ 19 _____ 10 -18 - 35

Pay _____

Account payee only

only

£

BERNARD DAVIES & SONS LTD

090925   10 18 35   68473841

NorthWest Bank PLC
Moston Branch
620 Lower High Street, Manchester M22 8RJ

date _____ 19 _____ 10 -18 - 35

Pay _____

Account payee only

only

£

BERNARD DAVIES & SONS LTD

090926   10 18 35   68473841

NorthWest Bank PLC
Moston Branch
620 Lower High Street, Manchester M22 8RJ

date _____ 19 _____ 10 -18 - 35

Pay _____

Account payee only

only

£

BERNARD DAVIES & SONS LTD

090927   10 18 35   68473841

4.2   Enter the details of the cheque payments from the last Task into the payments cash book shown below.

CASH BOOK – PAYMENTS			
Date	Cheque no.	Payee	Amount (£)

4.3   Complete a remittance advice for each of these three suppliers:

G M Trading Co Ltd

773 Broad Street, Salford M5 9DD

Northern Textile Company

601 Bacup Road, Blackburn BB6 4AJ

Barry Smart Limited

73 Station Road, Harrogate HG7 6PD

REMITTANCE ADVICE
BERNARD DAVIES & SONS LIMITED
701 FAULKNER STREET MANCHESTER M4 8DY
Tel 0161 428 2051 Fax 0161 428 2053
VAT Reg GB 929384746

TO

Cheque No

Date

date	your ref.	amount	discount	payment

cheque value £

REMITTANCE ADVICE
BERNARD DAVIES & SONS LIMITED
701 FAULKNER STREET MANCHESTER M4 8DY
Tel 0161 428 2051 Fax 0161 428 2053
VAT Reg GB 929384746

TO

Cheque No

Date

date	your ref.	amount	discount	payment

cheque value £

REMITTANCE ADVICE
BERNARD DAVIES & SONS LIMITED
701 FAULKNER STREET MANCHESTER M4 8DY
Tel 0161 428 2051 Fax 0161 428 2053
VAT Reg GB 929384746

TO

Cheque No

Date

date	your ref.	amount	discount	payment

cheque value   £

DEVOLVED ASSESSMENT TASKS – HORNET STATIONERY

The table below lists the performance criteria that are covered by the tasks. The relevant tasks are listed in the right-hand column.

UNIT 2 RECORDING AND ACCOUNTING FOR CREDIT TRANSACTIONS

element 1

process documents relating to goods and services supplied on credit   **task**

❑ *invoices and credit notes are correctly authorised and coded, and despatched to customers*   *2.1,2.2*

❑ *the calculations on invoices and credit notes, including discounts and VAT, are correct*   *2.1,2.2*

❑ *invoices and credit notes are correctly entered as primary accounting records in a form acceptable to the organisation*   *2.3*

❑ *the analysis and totalling of the primary record is completed accurately*   *2.3*

❑ *the organisation's procedures and timescales are observed*   *2.1,2.2,2.3*

❑ *discrepancies, unusual features or queries are identified and either resolved or referred to the appropriate person*   *2.2*

element 2

process documents relating to goods and services received on credit

❑ *suppliers' invoices and credit notes are correctly checked against ordering documentation and evidence that goods/services have been received*   *1.1*

❑ *suppliers' invoices and credit notes are correctly coded*   *1.1*

❑ *calculations on suppliers' invoices and credit notes are correct*   *1.1*

❑ *documents are correctly entered as primary accounting records in a form acceptable to the organisation*   *1.3*

❑ *the organisation's procedures and timescales are observed*   *1.1,1.2,1.3,1.4,3.1*

❑ *discrepancies, unusual features or queries are identified and either resolved or referred to the appropriate person*   *1.2*

element 3

account for goods and services supplied on credit

❏ *entries in the primary records are correctly transferred to the correct ledger accounts*   *2.4,3.1*

❏ *adjustments involving debtors' accounts are properly authorised and documented, and are correctly transferred to the correct ledger accounts*   *1.6*

❏ *the control account in the general ledger is reconciled with the total of balances in the sales (debtors) ledger*   *3.2*

❏ *where required, statements of account are sent to debtors promptly*   *3.4*

❏ *the organisation's procedures and timescales are observed*   *1.6,2.4,3.1,3.2*

❏ *discrepancies, unusual features or queries are identified and either resolved or referred to the appropriate person*   *1.6*

❏ *communications with debtors regarding accounts are handled promptly, courteously and effectively*   *3.4*

element 4

account for goods and services received on credit

❏ *entries in the primary records are correctly transferred to the correct ledger accounts*   *1.5,3.1*

❏ *adjustments involving creditors' accounts are properly authorised and documented, and are correctly transferred to the correct ledger accounts*   *1.6*

❏ *the control account in the general ledger is reconciled with the total of balances in the purchases (creditors) ledger*   *3.3*

❏ *the organisation's procedures and timescales are observed*   *1.5,1.6,3.3*

❏ *discrepancies, unusual features or queries are identified and either resolved or referred to the appropriate person*   *1.6*

❏ *communications with creditors regarding accounts are handled promptly, courteously and effectively*   *1.2*

INTRODUCTION

Your name is P Holder and you are the book-keeper for a wholesaler of stationery, office equipment and accessories: Hornet Stationery Limited, 29 Vicarage Road, Watford WD3 7AR. Today's date is Friday 25 July 1997.

Your duties as book-keeper include:

- checking suppliers' invoices by reference to goods received documentation (which must be signed by the goods-in manager, R Murdoch), and suppliers' terms and conditions. You are also required to check the calculations on suppliers' invoices before passing them to the Accountant, C Holton for payment.

- preparing sales invoices and credit notes by reference to despatch notes, goods returned notes (which must be signed by the goods-in manager, R Murdoch) and the company's price list.

- posting sales and purchase invoices and credit notes as well as any necessary adjustments, to ledger accounts. Note than any adjustments to the ledger accounts, other than those which derive from routine postings from the books of prime entry, must be authorised in writing by the Accountant.

SALES AND PURCHASES

Sales are analysed into three categories:

(a)   stationery (product codes beginning with S)

(b)   office equipment (product codes beginning with E)

(c)   accessories (product codes beginning with A)

All sales are subject to VAT at 17.5%

Purchases of goods for resale are analysed into the same three categories as sales.

LEDGERS

The company maintains a nominal (general) ledger together with memorandum sales and purchases ledgers.

PART ONE

1.1   Refer to the suppliers' invoices and related goods received notes on pages 127-132. The goods received notes have already been checked against the purchase orders. You are required to perform your usual validation checks on the invoices and to set out your results on the form provided on page 133. You should indicate either that the invoice is approved for payment, or that it is not approved. If it is not approved, you should state clearly the reason(s) why you are not approving it, and the follow-up action you would take.

INVOICE

FURLONG LIMITED

37 Highfield Trading Estate Lampeter LL4 7YG

invoice to		
Hornet Stationery Limited 29 Vicarage Road Watford WD3 7AR		

invoice no	7724
account	246
your reference	377
date/tax point	21 07 97

product code	description	quantity	price	unit	total	discount 0%	net
844	Calculator SRP22	30	6.10	each	183.00	0.00	183.00
2634	Dictaphone Z11	25	42.00	each	1050.00	0.00	1050.00
					goods total		1233.00
					VAT		215.77
					TOTAL		1448.77

terms
Net 30 days

INVOICE

Sheppard & Suckling

Hanover House, Lilly Square, London SW3 6BZ

invoice to		
Hornet Stationery Limited 29 Vicarage Road Watford WD3 7AR		

invoice no	2705
account	4226
your reference	390
date/tax point	22 07 97

product code	description	quantity	price	unit	total	discount 5%	net
B34	Laminated UK map	8	8.80	each	70.40	3.52	66.88
R219	A2 Desk planner	12	9.60	each	115.20	5.76	109.44
					goods total		176.32
					VAT		30.85
					TOTAL		207.17

terms
Net 30 days

INVOICE
Drysdale & Co
13 Berkeley Street, London E4 3BZ

invoice to

Hornet Stationery Limited
29 Vicarage Road
Watford
WD3 7AR

invoice no	2721
account	5291
your reference	364
date/tax point	21 07 97

product code	description	quantity	price	unit	total	discount 2%	net
5R80	White copy paper 80g	30	5.60	box	280.00	5.60	274.40
MEC5	Manila envelopes C5	50	7.30	box	365.00	7.30	357.70
					goods total		632.10
					VAT		108.95
					TOTAL		741.05

terms
1.5% cash discount 10 day settlement,
Net 30 days

INVOICE
Drysdale & Co
13 Berkeley Street, London E4 3BZ

invoice to

Hornet Stationery Limited
29 Vicarage Road
Watford
WD3 7AR

invoice no	2849
account	5291
your reference	402
date/tax point	21 07 97

product code	description	quantity	price	unit	total	discount 2%	net
T4000	Tabulabels, 4000 box	40	14.25	box	570.00	11.40	558.60
FX98	Calculator FX98	30	4.80	each	144.00	2.88	141.12
					goods total		699.72
					VAT		120.61
					TOTAL		820.33

terms
1.5% cash discount 10 day settlement,
Net 30 days

INVOICE
Soloman Limited
Bevels Drive, Hornsea, N11 5TG

invoice to

Hornet Stationery Limited
29 Vicarage Road
Watford
WD3 7AR

invoice no	149
account	435
your reference	381
date/tax point	21 07 97

product code	description	quantity	price	unit	total	discount 0%	net
180	Photocopier FP180	2	485.00	each	970.00	0.00	970.00
					goods total		970.00

terms
Net 30 days

VAT	169.75
TOTAL	1139.75

INVOICE
Nogan Limited
316 Pearse Road, Jackleton AD3 4PY

invoice to

Hornet Stationery Limited
29 Vicarage Road
Watford
WD3 7AR

invoice no	516
account	3241
your reference	385
date/tax point	21 07 97

product code	description	quantity	price	unit	total	discount 0%	net
244	Flexi desk light	4	23.00	each	92.00	0.00	92.00
234	Floor uplighter	6	18.50	each	111.00	0.00	111.00
441	Bubble jet printer	1	175.00	each	175.00	0.00	175.00
					goods total		378.00

terms
Net 30 days

VAT	66.15
TOTAL	444.15

INVOICE

Putney Limited
Unit 17 Bancroft Estate
Droysley MD14 6ZX

invoice to

Hornet Stationery Limited
29 Vicarage Road
Watford
WD3 7AR

invoice no	3492
account	4216
your reference	388
date/tax point	21 07 97

product code	description	quantity	price	unit	total	discount 3%	net
67B	Box files	120	2.10	each	252.00	7.56	244.44
442	Portable fan	6	18.00	each	108.00	3.24	104.76
					goods total		349.20

terms
Net 30 days

VAT	61.11
TOTAL	410.31

INVOICE

Meara Limited

45 Crystal Dock,
Thimborough BD17 2ER

invoice to

Hornet Stationery Limited
29 Vicarage Road
Watford
WD3 7AR

invoice no	423
account	2711
your reference	392
date/tax point	21 07 97

product code	description	quantity	price	unit	total	discount 5%	net
LP34	Laser printer	2	380.00	each	760.00	38.00	722.00
					goods total		722.00

terms
Net 30 days

VAT	126.35
TOTAL	848.35

GOODS RECEIVED NOTE   no 2143

Date	21 July 1997
Supplier	Drysdale & Co
Order no.	364

quantity	description
30 boxes	White copy paper 80g
50 boxes	Manila envelopes C5

received in good condition

R Murdoch

GOODS RECEIVED NOTE   no 2144

Date	21 July 1997
Supplier	Soloman Ltd
Order no.	381

quantity	description
2	Photocopier FP180

received in good condition

R Murdoch

GOODS RECEIVED NOTE   no 2145

Date	21 July 1997
Supplier	Nogan Ltd
Order no.	385

quantity	description
4	Flexi desk light
6	Floor uplighter

received in good condition

R Murdoch

GOODS RECEIVED NOTE   no 2146

Date	21 July 1997
Supplier	Furlong Ltd
Order no.	377

quantity	description
30	Calculator SRP22
25	Dictaphone Z11

received in good condition

R Murdoch

GOODS RECEIVED NOTE	no 2147

Date	21 July 1997
Supplier	Putney Ltd
Order no.	388

quantity	description
120	Box files
6	Portable fans

received in good condition

R Murdoch

GOODS RECEIVED NOTE	no 2148

Date	21 July 1997
Supplier	Meara Ltd
Order no.	392

quantity	description
2	Laser Printer

received in good condition

R Murdoch

GOODS RECEIVED NOTE	no 2149

Date	21 July 1997
Supplier	Sheppard & Suckling
Order no.	390

quantity	description
8	Laminated UK map
12	A2 Desk planner

received in good condition

R Murdoch

GOODS RECEIVED NOTE	no 2150

Date	21 July 1997
Supplier	Drysdale & Co
Order no.	402

quantity	description
40 boxes	Tabulabels
30	Calculator FX98

received in good condition

R Murdoch

Supplier/invoice	Action

1.2 In respect of any one invoice which you have not approved, you are required to write an appropriate letter to the supplier setting out the problem and calling for the appropriate action to be taken. Use the letterhead shown below for your answer.

HORNET STATIONERY LIMITED
29 Vicarage Road
Watford
WD3 7AR
Tel 01923 230399 Fax 01923 237995
VAT Reg 37 6171 89

HORNET STATIONERY LIMITED
Registered Office 29 Vicarage Road, Watford, WD3 7AR. Registered in England No 21134571

1.3   Refer to the purchases day book (below) which has already been written up to 24 July 1997.

You are required to enter all the invoices you have approved in task 1 in the purchases day book, including full analysis into the appropriate columns, and then to total the book for the week ended 25 July 1997. (In analysing the items purchased you will find it helpful to refer to the extract from Hornet Stationery's Price List on page 148).

PURCHASES DAY BOOK						
PURCHASES DAY BOOK						
Date 1997	Supplier	Total £	VAT £	Stationery £	Equipment £	Accessories £	Other £
21 July	Sheppard & Suckling	959.45	142.89	396.54		420.02	
21 July	Dyer Insurance Plc	270.00					270.00
22 July	Nogan Limited	2902.39	432.27		2470.12		
23 July	Meara Limited	1408.19	209.73	1198.46			
24 July	Drysdale & Co	324.77	48.37			276.40	
24 July	Furlong Limited	7446.91	1109.11		6337.80		
24 July	Putney Limited	971.45	144.68	826.77			

1.4 Refer to the purchases returns day book (below), which has been written up for the week ended Friday 25 July 1997. You are required to total the book.

		PURCHASES RETURNS DAY BOOK					
Date 1997	Supplier	Total £	VAT £	Stationery £	Equipment £	Accessories £	Other £
21 July	Soloman Limited	115.62	17.22			98.40	
24 July	Meara Limited	78.30	11.66	66.64			
24 July	Nogan Limited	104.45	15.55	88.90			

1.5   You are required to post the suppliers' invoices and credit notes for the week ended Friday 25 July 1997 to the memorandum purchases ledger accounts set out below.

Dr   **Drysdale & Co**   Cr

Date	Details	Amount	Date	Details	Amount
1997 23 Jul	Cash	£ 1460.00	1997 18 Jul	Balance b/f	£ 2170.41

Dr   **Dyer Insurance plc**   Cr

Date	Details	Amount	Date	Details	Amount
1997 22 Jul	Cash	£ 210.65	1997 18 Jul	Balance b/f	£ 210.65

Dr   **Furlong Ltd**   Cr

Date	Details	Amount	Date	Details	Amount
1997		£	1997 18 Jul	Balance b/f	£ 862.41

Dr **Meara Limited** Cr

Date	Details	Amount	Date	Details	Amount
1997		£	1997 18 Jul	Balance b/f	£ 1940.62

Dr **Nogan Limited** Cr

Date	Details	Amount	Date	Details	Amount
1997 21 Jul	Cash	£ 1973.22	1997 18 Jul	Balance b/f	£ 3265.20

Dr **Putney Limited** Cr

Date	Details	Amount	Date	Details	Amount
1997		£	1997 18 Jul	Balance b/f	£ 562.29

Dr   **Sheppard & Suckling**   Cr

Date	Details	Amount	Date	Details	Amount
1997		£	1997 18 Jul	Balance b/f	£ 3084.17

Dr   **Soloman Limited**   Cr

Date	Details	Amount	Date	Details	Amount
1997 22 Jul	Cash	£ 1491.27	1997 18 Jul	Balance b/f	£ 2865.23

Dr   **Other creditors**   Cr

Date	Details	Amount	Date	Details	Amount
1997 22 Jul	Cash	£ 6421.85	1997 18 Jul	Balance b/f	£ 13241.63

1.6   Refer to the memo from C Holton shown below. You are required to take the appropriate action to deal with it. (See pages 155-157 for the sales ledger accounts of Hornet Stationery Limited).

You should then total the purchases ledger accounts and bring down a balance on each as at 25 July 1997.

MEMORANDUM

To: P Holder, book-keeper

From: C Holton, Accountant

Date: 25 July 1997

Subject: Soloman Limited

As you know, there has been a balance outstanding on our sales ledger for some time now in respect of Soloman Limited. It's unlikely that they will be buying from us again, and I want to close the account down. I have their agreement to offset the balance against the amount we owe them in our purchases ledger, and I would be grateful if you would make the appropriate entries in the ledgers.

PART TWO

2.1   Refer to the despatch notes on the following pages. You are required to prepare sales invoices on the forms provided on pages 143 to 146. The invoices should be dated 25 July and numbered consecutively, beginning with number 2183.

You will need to refer to the customer details on page 147 and the extract from the Hornet price list on page 148.

DESPATCH NOTE   no 2142
Hornet Stationery, 29 Vicarage Road, Watford WD3 7AR

date 25 July 1997   **order ref** 517
to

Slinn Ltd
256 Highbrow Road
Muckleton
WW4 3QP

quantity	description	item code
6	White copy paper 100gsm 5 ream box	S016
1	Cash register ER165	E216

DESPATCH NOTE   no 2143
Hornet Stationery, 29 Vicarage Road, Watford WD3 7AR

date 25 July 1997   **order ref** 393
to

Lavin & Porter
Redbridge Road
Bushey
Herts BB7 2KL

quantity	description	item code
2	Hat/coat stand	A241
6	Telephone index	A804

DESPATCH NOTE   no 2144
Hornet Stationery, 29 Vicarage Road, Watford WD3 7AR

date 25 July 1997   **order ref** 217
to

Charlery Ltd
Unit 4
Enderby Trading Estate
Wicklop MB2 4RT

quantity	description	item code
12	Manila envelopes DL size box of 500	S107
15	Bubble envelopes 36x44mm, box of 100	S140

DESPATCH NOTE   no 2145
Hornet Stationery, 29 Vicarage Road, Watford WD3 7AR

date 25 July 1997   **order ref** 9001
to

Page Ltd
47 Brooking Road
Anderton
TY3 4AW

quantity	description	item code
1	Bubble jet printer	E418
4	Flexi desk light	A771

DESPATCH NOTE   no 2146

Hornet Stationery, 29 Vicarage Road, Watford WD3 7AR

date 25 July 1997   **order ref** 273

to

Bazeley Ltd
Unit 25 Hanbury Trading Estate
Marcham
LU6 4DR

quantity	description	item code
12	Wages book	S411
8	Calculator FX98	E097
2	Floor uplighter	A778

DESPATCH NOTE   no 2147

Hornet Stationery, 29 Vicarage Road, Watford WD3 7AR

date 25 July 1997   **order ref** 496

to

Holdsworth Ltd
212 Bankside Road
Slough
SL2 3MN

quantity	description	item code
12	White envelopes C4 box of 250	S132
4	Tabulabels, box of 4,000	S222

DESPATCH NOTE   no 2148

Hornet Stationery, 29 Vicarage Road, Watford WD3 7AR

date 25 July 1997   **order ref** 532

to

Slinn Ltd
256 Highbrow Road
Muckleton
WW4 3QP

quantity	description	item code
16	Box file, burgundy	S423
2	Dictaphone Z11	E601

DESPATCH NOTE   no 2149

Hornet Stationery, 29 Vicarage Road, Watford WD3 7AR

date 25 July 1997   **order ref** 4441

to

Hessenthaler & Co
64 Brackley Street
Luton
LU3 9GH

quantity	description	item code
20	White copy paper 80gsm 5 ream box	S012
1	Photocopier FP180	E323

HORNET STATIONERY LIMITED   *invoice*

29 Vicarage Road
Watford
WD3 7AR
Tel 01923 230399 Fax 01923 237995
VAT Reg 37 6171 89

to:

invoice no

account

your reference

date/tax point

item code	description	quantity	price	unit	total	discount	net
					goods total		
terms:					**VAT**		
					TOTAL		

HORNET STATIONERY LIMITED   *invoice*

29 Vicarage Road
Watford
WD3 7AR
Tel 01923 230399 Fax 01923 237995
VAT Reg 37 6171 89

to:

invoice no

account

your reference

date/tax point

item code	description	quantity	price	unit	total	discount	net
					goods total		
terms:					**VAT**		
					TOTAL		

HORNET STATIONERY LIMITED

invoice

29 Vicarage Road
Watford
WD3 7AR
Tel 01923 230399 Fax 01923 237995
VAT Reg 37 6171 89

to:

invoice no

account

your reference

date/tax point

item code	description	quantity	price	unit	total	discount	net
					goods total		
terms:					**VAT**		
					TOTAL		

HORNET STATIONERY LIMITED

invoice

29 Vicarage Road
Watford
WD3 7AR
Tel 01923 230399 Fax 01923 237995
VAT Reg 37 6171 89

to:

invoice no

account

your reference

date/tax point

item code	description	quantity	price	unit	total	discount	net
					goods total		
terms:					**VAT**		
					TOTAL		

HORNET STATIONERY LIMITED

invoice

29 Vicarage Road
Watford
WD3 7AR
Tel 01923 230399 Fax 01923 237995
VAT Reg 37 6171 89

to:

invoice no

account

your reference

date/tax point

item code	description	quantity	price	unit	total	discount	net
					goods total		
terms:					**VAT**		
					TOTAL		

HORNET STATIONERY LIMITED

invoice

29 Vicarage Road
Watford
WD3 7AR
Tel 01923 230399 Fax 01923 237995
VAT Reg 37 6171 89

to:

invoice no

account

your reference

date/tax point

item code	description	quantity	price	unit	total	discount	net
					goods total		
terms:					**VAT**		
					TOTAL		

HORNET STATIONERY LIMITED   *invoice*

29 Vicarage Road
Watford
WD3 7AR
Tel 01923 230399 Fax 01923 237995
VAT Reg 37 6171 89

to:

invoice no

account

your reference

date/tax point

item code	description	quantity	price	unit	total	discount	net

goods total	
VAT	
TOTAL	

terms:

HORNET STATIONERY LIMITED   *invoice*

29 Vicarage Road
Watford
WD3 7AR
Tel 01923 230399 Fax 01923 237995
VAT Reg 37 6171 89

to:

invoice no

account

your reference

date/tax point

item code	description	quantity	price	unit	total	discount	net

goods total	
VAT	
TOTAL	

terms:

HORNET STATIONERY LIMITED

CUSTOMER DETAILS

Name	Address	Trade Discount
Charlery Ltd	Unit 4 Enderby Trading Estate Wicklop MB2 4RT	5%
Slinn Ltd	256 Highbrow Road Muckleton WW4 3QP	8%
Hessenthaler & Co	64 Brackley Street Luton LU3 9GH	*4%
Bazeley Ltd	Unit 25 Hanbury Trading Estate Marcham LU6 4DR	7%
Lavin & Porter	Redbridge Road Bushey BB7 2KL	10%
Holdsworth Ltd	212 Bankside Road Slough SL2 3MN	6%
Page Ltd	47 Brooking Road Anderton TY3 4AW	7.5%

*Hessenthaler & Co also received a 2% cash discount for settlement within 10 days. Otherwise, Hornet's terms are always net, 30 days.

EXTRACTS FROM THE HORNET STATIONERY PRICE LIST

Item description	Item code	Price (excl VAT)
		£
Stationery		
White copy paper, 80 gsm, 5 ream box	S012	7.40
White copy paper, 100 gsm, 5 ream box	S016	12.20
Manila envelopes, DL size, box of 500	S107	15.20
Manila envelopes, C5 size, box of 250	S121	10.25
White envelopes, C4 size, box of 250	S132	12.50
Bubble envelopes, 36 x 44 mm, box of 100	S140	7.80
Tabulabels, box of 4,000	S222	20.50
A4 refill pads, 80 leaves, pack of 10	S306	4.80
Wages book	S411	4.30
Box file	S423	3.60
Office equipment		
Calculator FX98	E097	6.90
Calculator SRP 22	E099	8.20
Cash register ER165	E216	160.00
Photocopier FP180	E323	645.00
Bubble jet printer	E418	240.00
Laser printer	E456	524.00
Dictaphone Z11	E601	66.00
Accessories		
Hat/coat stand	A241	23.00
Hi-tech clock	A376	6.50
Laminated UK map	A412	12.60
Portable fan	A500	26.00
A2 desk planner	A623	14.25
Flexi desk light	A771	31.50
Floor uplighter	A778	27.00
Telephone index	A804	6.80

2.2   Refer to the goods returned notes on page 150 Provided you are satisfied with them, you are required to prepare credit notes using the forms provided on pages 151 and 152. You should number the credit notes consecutively, beginning with number 231.

If you are not satisfied with the goods returned documentation, explain what action you would take using the schedule shown below.

Goods returned note	Action

GOODS RETURNED NOTE

date 25 July 1997
from:

Bazeley Limited
Unit 25 Hanbury Trading Estate
Marcham
LU6 4DR

quantity	description	item code
2	A4 refill pads, 80 leaves, pack of 10	S306

Received in good condition .... *R Murdoch* ....

GOODS RETURNED NOTE

date 25 July 1997
from:

Holdswoth Limited
212 Bankside Road
Slough
SL2 3MN

quantity	description	item code
1	Dictaphone Z11	E601
2	Hi-tech clocks	A376

Received in good condition .... *R Murdoch* ....

GOODS RETURNED NOTE

date 25 July 1997
from:

Charlery Limited
Unit 4
Enderby Trading Estate
Wicklop MB2 4RT

quantity	description	item code
3	Calculator FX98	E097

Received in good condition ....

GOODS RETURNED NOTE

date 25 July 1997
from:

Page Limited
47 Brooking Road
Anderton
TY3 4AW

quantity	description	item code
2	A2 desk planner	A623

Received in good condition .... *R Murdoch* ....

HORNET STATIONERY LIMITED   *credit note*

29 Vicarage Road
Watford
WD3 7AR
Tel 01923 230399 Fax 01923 237995
VAT Reg 37 6171 89

to:

credit note no

account

date/tax point

item code	description	quantity	price	unit	total	discount	net
					goods total		
reason for credit:					**VAT**		
					TOTAL		

HORNET STATIONERY LIMITED   *credit note*

29 Vicarage Road
Watford
WD3 7AR
Tel 01923 230399 Fax 01923 237995
VAT Reg 37 6171 89

to:

credit note no

account

date/tax point

item code	description	quantity	price	unit	total	discount	net
					goods total		
reason for credit:					**VAT**		
					TOTAL		

HORNET STATIONERY LIMITED   *credit note*

29 Vicarage Road
Watford
WD3 7AR
Tel 01923 230399 Fax 01923 237995
VAT Reg 37 6171 89

to: credit note no

                                 account

                                 date/tax point

item code	description	quantity	price	unit	total	discount	net

	goods total	
reason for credit:	VAT	
	TOTAL	

HORNET STATIONERY LIMITED   *credit note*

29 Vicarage Road
Watford
WD3 7AR
Tel 01923 230399 Fax 01923 237995
VAT Reg 37 6171 89

to: credit note no

                                 account

                                 date/tax point

item code	description	quantity	price	unit	total	discount	net

	goods total	
reason for credit:	VAT	
	TOTAL	

2.3   Refer to the sales day book and the sales returns day book on the next page, which have already been written up to 24 July 1997.

You are required to enter all the invoices and credit notes for 25 July 1997 in the day books, including full analysis into the appropriate columns, and then to total the two books for the week ended 25 July 1997.

SALES DAY BOOK							
Date 1997	Invoice	Customer	Total £	VAT £	Stationery £	Equipment £	Accessories £
21 July	2174	Bazeley Ltd	430.69	64.14	241.90		124.65
21 July	2175	Charlery Ltd	2731.25	406.78		1947.60	376.87
21 July	2176	Page Ltd	651.04	96.96	554.08		
22 July	2177	Hessenthaler & Co	1291.33	192.32	354.12	744.89	
23 July	2178	Lavin & Porter	498.05	74.17			423.88
23 July	2179	Holdsworth Ltd	3131.16	466.34		2664.82	
24 July	2180	Slinn Ltd	1058.95	157.71	804.22		97.02
24 July	2181	Hessenthaler & Co	504.50	75.13	76.43	238.08	114.86
24 July	2182	Holdsworth Ltd	2148.79	320.03	642.22	1186.54	

SALES RETURNS DAY BOOK							
Date 1997	Credit note	Customer	Total £	VAT £	Stationery £	Equipment £	Accessories £
21 July	227	Holdsworth Ltd	87.18	12.98	74.20		
22 July	228	Slinn Ltd	148.05	22.05		126.00	
24 July	229	Lavin & Porter	52.73	7.85			44.88
24 July	230	Page Ltd	57.12	8.50	48.62		

2.4   You are required to post the invoices and credit notes for the week ended Friday 25 July 1997 to the memorandum sales ledger accounts on the following pages, and then to total the accounts, bringing down a balance on each as at close of business on 25 July 1997.

Dr   **Charlery Limited**   Cr

Date	Details	Amount	Date	Details	Amount
1997 18 Jul	Balance b/f	£ 1752.09	1997 22 Jul	Cash	£ 851.32

Dr   **Slinn Ltd**   Cr

Date	Details	Amount	Date	Details	Amount
1997 18 Jul	Balance b/f	£ 2960.27	1997		£

Dr   **Hessenthaler & Co**   Cr

Date	Details	Amount	Date	Details	Amount
1997 18 Jul	Balance b/f	£ 862.12	1997		£

Dr   **Bazeley Ltd**   Cr

Date	Details	Amount	Date	Details	Amount
1997 18 Jul	Balance b/f	£ 741.89	1997 21 Jul	Cash	£ 296.25

Dr   **Soloman Ltd**   Cr

Date	Details	Amount	Date	Details	Amount
1997 18 Jul	Balance b/f	£ 78.93	1997		£

Dr   **Lavin & Porter**   Cr

Date	Details	Amount	Date	Details	Amount
1997 18 Jul	Balance b/f	£ 2108.65	1997 23 Jul	Cash	£ 560.24

Dr   **Holdsworth Ltd**   Cr

Date	Details	Amount	Date	Details	Amount
1997 18 Jul	Balance b/f	£ 1009.62	1997		£

Dr   **Page Ltd**   Cr

Date	Details	Amount	Date	Details	Amount
1997 18 Jul	Balance b/f	£ 922.46	1997		£

Dr   **Other debtors**   Cr

Date	Details	Amount	Date	Details	Amount
1997 18 Jul	Balance b/f	£ 13601.27	1997 23 Jul	Cash	£ 6311.15

PART THREE

3.1   You are required to post the totals of the sales day book, purchases day book, sales returns day book and purchases returns day book for the week ended Friday 25 July 1997 to the nominal (general) ledger accounts on the following pages.

Dr   **Sales: stationery**   Cr

Date	Details	Amount	Date	Details	Amount
1997		£	1997 18 Jul	Balance b/f	£ 97241.28

Dr   **Sales: equipment**   Cr

Date	Details	Amount	Date	Details	Amount
1997		£	1997 18 Jul	Balance b/f	£ 63891.25

Dr   **Sales: accessories**   Cr

Date	Details	Amount	Date	Details	Amount
1997		£	1997 18 Jul	Balance b/f	£ 46190.88

Dr   **Purchases: stationery**   Cr

Date	Details	Amount	Date	Details	Amount
1997 18 Jul	Balance b/f	£ 62057.81	1997		£

Dr   **Purchases: equipment**   Cr

Date	Details	Amount	Date	Details	Amount
1997 18 Jul	Balance b/f	£ 45217.84	1997		£

Dr   **Purchases: accessories**   Cr

Date	Details	Amount	Date	Details	Amount
1997 18 Jul	Balance b/f	£ 23421.66	1997		£

Dr   **Sales returns: stationery**   Cr

Date	Details	Amount	Date	Details	Amount
1997 18 Jul	Balance b/f	£ 2471.13	1997		£

Dr   **Sales returns: equipment**   Cr

Date	Details	Amount	Date	Details	Amount
1997 18 Jul	Balance b/f	£ 3250.07	1997		£

Dr   **Sales returns: accessories**   **Cr**

Date	Details	Amount	Date	Details	Amount
1997 18 Jul	Balance b/f	£ 832.19	1997		£

Dr   **Purchases returns: stationery**   **Cr**

Date	Details	Amount	Date	Details	Amount
1997		£	1997 18 Jul	Balance b/f	£ 2951.54

Dr   **Purchases returns: equipment**   **Cr**

Date	Details	Amount	Date	Details	Amount
1997		£	1997 18 Jul	Balance b/f	£ 3441.26

Dr   **Purchases returns: accessories**   Cr

Date	Details	Amount	Date	Details	Amount
1997		£	1997 18 Jul	Balance b/f	£ 841.26

Dr   **Insurance**   Cr

Date	Details	Amount	Date	Details	Amount
1997 18 Jul	Balance b/f	£ 1692.37	1997		£

Dr   **VAT**   Cr

Date	Details	Amount	Date	Details	Amount
1997		£	1997 18 Jul	Balance b/f	£ 2471.26

Dr   **Sales ledger control**   Cr

Date	Details	Amount	Date	Details	Amount
1997 18 Jul	Balance b/f	£ 24037.30	1997 25 Jul	Cash received	£ 8018.96

Dr   **Purchases ledger control**   Cr

Date	Details	Amount	Date	Details	Amount
1997 25 Jul	Cash paid	£ 11556.99	1997 18 Jul	Balance b/f	£ 28202.61

3.2   You are required to extract and total a list of balances from the sales ledger as at 25 July 1997 and agree the total of your listing with the total indicated by the sales ledger control account. Use the column provided for your answer.

Sales ledger: list of balances

	At 18 July £	At 25 July £
Charlery Ltd	1,752.09	
Slinn Ltd	2,960.27	
Hessenthaler & Co	862.12	
Bazeley Ltd	741.89	
Soloman Ltd	78.93	
Lavin & Porter	2,108.65	
Holdsworth Ltd	1,009.62	
Page Ltd	922.46	
Other debtors	13,601.27	_____
	24,037.30	========

3.3   You are required to extract and total a list of balances from the purchases ledger as at 25 July 1997 and agree the total of your listing with the total indicated by the purchases ledger control account. Use the column provided for your answer.

Purchases ledger: list of balances

	At 18 July £	At 25 July £
Drysdale & Co	2,170.41	
Dyer Insurance plc	210.65	
Furlong Ltd	862.41	
Meara Ltd	1,940.62	
Nogan Ltd	3,265.20	
Putney Ltd	562.29	
Sheppard & Suckling	3,084.17	
Soloman Ltd	2,865.23	
Other creditors	13,241.63	_____
	28,202.61	========

3.4   No payment has been received from Hessenthaler and Co since 31 January 1997, and until this week their balance remained unchanged at £862.12 ever since that date. C Holton has asked you to prepare a statement of account for this customer, together with a draft letter in his/her name requesting early payment of the overdue amount.

You are required to prepare the statement and the draft letter using the documents on the next two pages.

STATEMENT

HORNET STATIONERY LIMITED

29 Vicarage Road
Watford
WD3 7AR
Tel 01923 230399 Fax 01923 237995
VAT Reg 37 6171 89

to

date

date	details	debit £	credit £	balance £

AMOUNT NOW DUE	

HORNET STATIONERY LIMITED
29 Vicarage Road
Watford
WD3 7AR
Tel 01923 230399 Fax 01923 237995
VAT Reg 37 6171 89

HORNET STATIONERY LIMITED
Registered Office 29 Vicarage Road, Watford, WD3 7AR. Registered in England No 21134571

Section 3

central assessment processing exercises and short answer questions

The communication tasks which relate to these processing exercises follow in a separate section. Appropriate page references are to be found at the beginning of each set of processing exercises.

CENTRAL ASSESSMENT TASKS – CHANG FASHIONS LIMITED

1

Communication exercises relating to these tasks may be found on page 228

INTRODUCTION

The tasks and questions are based on the transactions of Chang Fashions Limited. The company owns a chain of clothes shops and has its head office located in London. The head office has good storage facilities for stock held, substantial sales area for both men's and ladies' wear and office space for the administrative staff employed within the company.

The Managing Director is Mary Chang and Rahul Divan is the Accountant and Company Secretary. You are employed as an Accounting Technician to assist Rahul Divan.

DATA

The following transactions all occurred during the week ended 2 December 1994 and have been entered for you into summarised books of original entry. VAT has been calculated to the nearest pound at a rate of 17.5% and you should continue to use this rate for any subsequent calculations.

'Other customers' and 'other suppliers' should each be treated as individual accounts.

PURCHASES INVOICES RECEIVED

	Total	VAT	Net	Goods for resale	Power and heating
	£	£	£	£	£
Style Clothes Ltd	9,736	1,450	8,286	8,286	
South East Electric	3,550	529	3,021		3,021
Southern Gas	3,108	463	2,645		2,645
Trend Imports Ltd	17,907	2,667	15,240	15,240	
Other suppliers	20,935	3,118	17,817	17,817	
	55,236	8,227	47,009	41,343	5,666

PURCHASES RETURNS DAY BOOK

	Total	VAT	Net
	£	£	£
Style Clothes Ltd	256	38	218

CASH BOOK

			£
Opening balance at start of the week			28,619 (credit)

Receipts	Total received	VAT	
	£	£	
Cash sales	52,170	7,770 44,400	
Bank interest	411		
		52,581	
		23,962	

Payments	Discount	Total paid	VAT	
	£	£	£	
Cash purchases		1,376	205 1171	
Style Clothes Ltd	160	7,420		
Southern Gas		1,204		
Shop fittings purchased		1,640	244 1,396	
Shop fittings repaired		88	13 75	
Refunds for returns Sales Return		275	41 234	
Other suppliers	12,143 ——→			

creditors

			24,146
Closing balance at end of week			184 (credit)

The following balances are available to you at the start of the week ended 2 December 1994:

Suppliers:	£
Style Clothes Ltd	32,417
South East Electric	3550 + NIL
Southern Gas	1,204
Trend Imports Ltd	17907 + 45,862
Other suppliers	98,291

Other:	£
Purchases	1,066,213
Sales	1,453,420 44,400
Purchases returns	5,741 + 218
Sales returns	6,984
Power and heating	7,122
Shop fittings	35,560
Shop fittings repairs	241 + 75
Bank interest received	319 + 411
VAT (credit balance)	38,162
Discount received	4,337 + 160
Creditors control account	177,774
Various other debit balances - total:	1,542,632
Various other credit balances - total:	950,380

PROCESSING EXERCISE

COMPLETE ALL THE FOLLOWING TASKS

Task 1   Enter the opening balances into the following accounts:

Creditors control account

Power and heating

Purchases

Sales returns

Shop fittings

VAT

Southern Gas

Style Clothes Ltd

These accounts can be found on the pages that follow.

Task 2   Enter all relevant entries into the accounts shown in task 1.

Task 3   Balance off all the accounts in which you have made entries in task 2.

Task 4   Calculate the closing balances of the remaining accounts. Complete the list of balances on page 174 by inserting the updated figure for each account in either the debit balances column or the credit balances column as appropriate. Total the two columns. The two totals should be the same. If they do not agree try to trace and correct any errors you may have made within the time you have available. If you are still unable to make the totals balance, leave the work incomplete. (In checking for errors you should take into account that the total of the suppliers' balances should be the same figure as the balance of the creditors control account).

NOTE   It is not a requirement to draw up all the individual accounts in order to calculate the closing balances for task 4. You may, however, adopt that approach if you wish.

GENERAL LEDGER

Dr   **Creditors Control Account**   Cr

Date	Details	Amount £	Date	Details	Amount £

Dr   **Power & Heating**   Cr

Date	Details	Amount £	Date	Details	Amount £

Dr   **Purchases**   Cr

Date	Details	Amount £	Date	Details	Amount £

Dr   **Sales Returns**   Cr

Date	Details	Amount £	Date	Details	Amount £

Dr   **Shop Fittings**   Cr

Date	Details	Amount £	Date	Details	Amount £

Dr   **VAT**   Cr

Date	Details	Amount £	Date	Details	Amount £

CREDITORS LEDGER

Dr   **Southern Gas**   Cr

Date	Details	Amount	Date	Details	Amount
		£			£

Dr   **Style Clothes Ltd**   Cr

Date	Details	Amount	Date	Details	Amount
		£			£

LIST OF UPDATED BALANCES AT THE END OF THE WEEK:

	Debit balances £	Credit balances £
Suppliers		
Style Clothes Ltd	....	....
South East Electric	....	....
Southern Gas	....	....
Trend Imports Ltd	....	....
Other suppliers	....	....
Total of suppliers	....	....
Other		
Bank	....	....
Purchases	....	....
Sales	....	....
Purchases returns	....	....
Sales returns	....	....
Power and heating	....	....
Shop fittings	....	....
Shop fittings repairs	....	....
Bank interest received	....	....
VAT	....	....
Discount received	....	....
Other debit balances	1,542,632	
Other credit balances		950,380
Totals		

SHORT ANSWER QUESTIONS

Using, where appropriate, the information given in the Processing Exercise, write on the dotted line or circle the correct answer.

1.1   If, at the end of the day on 2 December 1994, all the entries in the cash book match the entries which have passed through the bank statement apart from

(a) unpresented cheques for £30,291

and

(b) receipts not yet banked for £26,435,

what would be the balance shown on the bank statement as at 2 December 1994?

£.............................debit/credit

1.2   Would the bank interest of £411 shown in the cash book appear on the bank statement as a debit entry or a credit entry?

Debit entry/Credit entry

1.3   The cheque shown below has been issued by Chang Fashions Ltd.

Royal Bank PLC 61 Euston Road London NW1 4ER	date *15 November* 19 *94*	19 14 60
Pay *K Mitchell*		only
One hundred and fifty pounds only	National Bank Watford High Street	£ *150.00*
		CHANG FASHIONS LIMITED
		Mary Chang
098923 19 14 60 670981702		

Briefly explain the effect of the crossing –

....

....

1.4   Referring to the cheque shown in question 1.3, give the name of:

(a)   the drawer   ....

(b)   the drawee   ....

(c)   the payee   ....

1.5 The sales and purchases day books are primary records used for listing data taken from source documents. Double entry is carried out by transferring relevant totals from the day books into the general ledger.

True/False

1.6 List **three** checks that should be carried out specifically relating to the receipt of a cheque from a customer when the cheque is supported by a cheque guarantee card.

....

....

....

1.7 A customer wishes to purchase £320 of clothes from the shop using a credit card for payment. The floor limit set by the credit card company is £100.

(a) Is it possible that the transaction can still go ahead despite the floor limit?   Yes/No

(b) Briefly explain the reason for your answer.

....

....

1.8 Chang Fashions Ltd has recently purchased £10,000 of children's clothes (zero rated supplies). How much VAT will be collected from the sale of these clothes?   £...

1.9 On 2 November Mary Chang telephoned Andrew Potts, the owner of Potts Boutique, and offered to sell him some surplus stock for £2,500. Andrew replied that he wanted a few days to consider the offer and he agreed to send a written response through the post within a few days. He posted an acceptance of the offer on 8 November and this was received by Mary on 10 November. The clothes were delivered to Andrew on 15 November and payment was made on 22 November.

(a) On what date was a contract for the sale of the stock formed between Chang Fashions Ltd and Andrew Potts?

....

(b) Briefly explain the reason for your answer.

....

....

1.10 Mary Chang has decided that some of the offices are looking rather shabby. She arranges for the walls to be redecorated and for the purchase of some new office furniture.

(a) Is the cost of the redecoration capital or revenue expenditure?

Capital/Revenue

(b)   Is the cost of the new office furniture capital or revenue expenditure?

Capital/Revenue

1.11 Debit cards allow customers to use funds held in their bank accounts to make payments without the need to issue cheques.

True/False

1.12 A customer has come into the shop with a pair of jeans bought three days earlier. She complains that the zip has broken and she demands a refund. The cashier refuses and points to a sign on the wall which states:

"Goods bought in this shop will not be exchanged and refunds will not be made."

(a)   Would it appear that the customer is entitled to a refund?   Yes/No

(b)   Briefly explain the reason for your answer.

....

....

1.13 The company operates its petty cash using the imprest system. The imprest amount is £250.00. At the end of a particular period the five analysis columns were totalled to give the following amounts:

Column 1	£26.19
Column 2	£45.27
Column 3	£6.94
Column 4	£12.81
Column 5	£14.38

How much cash would be required to restore the imprest amount for the following period?

£.................................

1.14 The company receives an invoice from a supplier offering a 5% cash discount which amounts to £120. What would be the total of the invoice inclusive of VAT?

£.................................

1.15 Batch processing is a system whereby transactions are processed as and when they arise in order to keep the ledgers totally up to date.

True/False

1.16 The cashiers employed by Chang Fashions Ltd each have an electronic cash register. It is important for the company to ensure that the cashiers do not keep any of the cash handed over by the customers for themselves. Briefly describe what you consider should happen at the end of each day's trading as a system of control.

....

....

....

....

1.17 (a) A cheque issued by a bank and drawn upon itself is known as a

....

(b) Briefly explain the advantage to a creditor in receiving such a cheque from a debtor in preference to the debtor's own cheque.

....

....

1.18 Would the following accounts be found in the general ledger, the creditors ledger or the debtors ledger?

(a) Debtors control account ....

(b) Sales account ....

(c) Shop fittings repairs ....

1.19 Explain briefly why Chang Fashions Ltd might add 'E & OE' to invoices issued to customers.

....

....

1.20 A remittance advice is a document sent by a supplier to a customer to advise the customer that goods ordered have been sent off to the customer.

True/False

CENTRAL ASSESSMENT TASKS – COMART SUPPLIES LIMITED

Communication exercises relating to these tasks may be found on page 232

INTRODUCTION

The tasks and questions are based on the transactions of Comart Supplies Limited. The company operates as a distributor of computer hardware, software and general consumables. It is located in Taunton in the UK.

The Managing Director is Paul Byrne and Louise Ford is the Accountant. You are employed as an Accounting Technician to assist Louise Ford.

DATA

The following transactions all occurred on 1 June 1995 and have yet to be entered into the ledger system. VAT has been calculated to the nearest pound at a rate of 17.5% and you should continue to use this rate for any subsequent calculations. The bank statement was received on 2 June, but again contains transactions relating to 1 June.

SALES INVOICES ISSUED

	Total £	VAT £	Net £
Computer Care Ltd	9,655	1,438	8,217
Bristol Micros	8,100	1,206	6,894
Silicon World	6,753	1,005	5,748
Other customers	16,891	2,516	14,375
	41,399	6,165	35,234

PURCHASES INVOICES RECEIVED

	Total £	VAT £	Net £	Goods for resale £	Other items £
Smith Electronics Ltd	5,800	864	4,936	4,936	
ITC Computers Ltd	4,315	643	3,672	3,672	
Western Imports Ltd	11,266	1,678	9,588	9,588	
Other suppliers	13,148	1,958	11,190	10,090	1,100
	34,529	5,143	29,386	28,286	1,100

Analysis of other items purchased:

	£
Telephones	264
Power and heating	626
Sundry expenses	210
	1,100

CREDIT NOTE ISSUED

	Total	VAT	Net
	£	£	£
Silicon World	193	29	164

CREDIT NOTE RECEIVED

	Total	VAT	Net
	£	£	£
ITC Computers Ltd	660	98	562

JOURNAL ENTRIES

	Debit	Credit
	£	£
Bad debts	493	
Debtors control account		493

Software City (included in the balance of other customers) debt written off.

CHEQUES ISSUED

ITC Computers Ltd £3,240 (in full repayment of a debt for £3,340) *Discount Rec £100*

CHEQUES RECEIVED

Silicon World £6,024 (in full repayment of a debt for £6,275) *Discount All £251*
Bristol Micros £7,687
Cash sales £1,645 (inclusive of VAT of £245) *1,400 Sales*

ACCOUNT BALANCES

The following balances are available to you at the start of the day on 1 June 1995:

Customers:	£
Computer Care Ltd	45,261
Bristol Micros	32,310
Silicon World	29,873
Other customers	697,429
Suppliers:	
Smith Electronics Ltd	23,572
ITC Computers Ltd	25,689

Western Imports Ltd	56,734
Other suppliers	502,173
Other:	
Purchases	1,241,860
Sales	1,655,960
Purchases returns	7,798
Sales returns	8,346
Bank (credit balance)	4,670
Bank loan	16,200
Discount allowed	24,839
Discount received	18,628
Debtors control account	804,873
Creditors control account	608,168
VAT (credit balance)	69,173
Bad debts	nil
Telephones	nil
Power and heating	487
Sundry expenses	361
Various other debit balances - total:	1,362,347
Various other credit balances - total:	1,062,516

BANK STATEMENT RECEIVED

Midwest Bank plc
Comart Supplies Ltd
Statement of Account

Account No: 80148762

Date	Details	Debit	Credit	Balance
		£	£	£
1 June	Balance forward			3,465 O/D
1 June	Silicon World BGC		1,000	2,465 O/D
1 June	Loan Repayment TR	400		2,865 O/D
1 June	Cheque No. 302462	1,205		4,070 O/D

O/D Overdrawn	BGC Bank Giro Credit	TR Transfer

PROCESSING EXERCISE

COMPLETE ALL THE FOLLOWING TASKS

Task 1   Enter the opening balances into the following accounts:

Bank (cash book)

Bank loan

Debtors control account

Discount allowed

Discount received

Power and heating

Purchases

VAT

ITC Computers Ltd

These accounts can be found on pages 183 - 186.

Task 2   Using the data shown on pages 179 - 181, enter all relevant transactions into the accounts shown in task 1. Please note that the cash book has been divided into two sections, one to record receipts and the other to record payments. When making entries in the cash book ensure that you complete the analysis columns (used to analyse amounts received and amounts paid) and that you include the bank giro credit and loan repayment shown in the bank statement on page 181.

Task 3   Total the various columns of the cash book and clearly show the closing bank balance.

Task 4   Transfer any relevant sums from the cash book into the other accounts shown in task 1.

Task 5   Balance off all the remaining accounts in which you have made entries.

Note   You are not required to update any accounts other than those shown in task 1.

CASH BOOK

Receipts

Date	Details	Discounts £	Total rec'd £	VAT £	Debtors £	Other £

Payments

Date	Details	Discounts £	Total paid £	VAT £	Creditors £	Other £

GENERAL LEDGER

Dr   Bank loan   Cr

Date	Details	Amount £	Date	Details	Amount £

Dr   **Debtors control account**   Cr

Date	Details	Amount	Date	Details	Amount
		£			£

Dr   **Discount allowed**   Cr

Date	Details	Amount	Date	Details	Amount
		£			£

Dr   **Discount received**   Cr

Date	Details	Amount	Date	Details	Amount
		£			£

Dr   **Power and heating**   Cr

Date	Details	Amount	Date	Details	Amount
		£			£

Dr   **Purchases**   Cr

Date	Details	Amount	Date	Details	Amount
		£			£

Dr   **Sales**   Cr

Date	Details	Amount	Date	Details	Amount
		£			£

Dr   **VAT**   Cr

Date	Details	Amount £	Date	Details	Amount £

CREDITORS LEDGER

Dr   **ITC Computers Limited**   Cr

Date	Details	Amount £	Date	Details	Amount £

SHORT ANSWER QUESTIONS

Using, where appropriate, the information given in the Processing Exercise, write on the dotted lines or circle the correct answer.

2.1   If cheque number 302462 had been presented to the bank prior to 1 June, what would have been the opening balance of the bank statement shown on page 181?

£.4,670.........debit/~~credit~~   increase o/d

2.2   The bank giro credit and transfer shown on the bank statement were used to update the cash book. Explain briefly why it was not necessary to include cheque number 302462 in the updating process.

Entered in cash book when produced cheque ....

....

2.3   In preparing a bank reconciliation statement to agree the balance of the updated cash book with the balance of the bank statement:

(a)   Would the cheque for £3,240 payable to ITC Computers Ltd be added to or subtracted from the cash book balance?

Added/~~Subtracted~~

(b)   Would the receipts totalling £15,356 (£6,024 + £7,687 + £1,645) be added to or subtracted from the cash book balance?

~~Added~~/Subtracted

2.4   If a cheque received from a customer was subsequently returned unpaid by that customer's bank, would the unpaid entry appear as a debit or a credit on Comart Supplies Limited's bank statement?

Debit/Credit

2.5

		19–14–60
National Bank plc		25 May 1995
44, Wellington Road, Taunton		
Pay M Lewis only		
Two hundred and twenty pounds		£ 220.00
		S Ashley
		S Ashley
200550 19-14-60 50731247		

The reverse of the cheque has been signed 'M Lewis'.

(a)   Could the cheque be paid into Comart Supplies Ltd's bank account?

Yes/No

(b)   Briefly explain the reason for your answer.

Because the word 'only' appears after the payee's

name on the front of the cheque

2.6   The cheque shown in question 2.5 has two vertical lines printed on it to form a crossing. However, since there are no instructions between the lines, such as "not negotiable" or "account payee only", the crossing has no effect and the cheque can be cashed by the payee.

True/False

2.7   Comart Supplies Ltd has recently purchased five ITC computers. Would the purchase be regarded as capital expenditure or revenue expenditure if:

(a)   The computers are to be used for data processing by the company?

Capital/Revenue

(b)   The computers are to be held as stock for sale to customers?

Capital/Revenue

2.8   Software has been sold on credit to Softsell Ltd, a new small business which is not registered for VAT. The invoice shows the cost of the software as £160 plus £28 VAT giving a total of £188. In recording the transaction which general ledger account(s) will be debited and which will be credited:

(a)   In the books of Comart Supplies Ltd?

Debit	Credit
Debtors (Softsell Ltd)	*Sales*
Sales Ledger Control	*VAT*

(b)   In the books of Softsell Ltd?

Debit	Credit
Purchases	*Creditors (Comart Supplies Ltd)*
VAT X Not registered for Vat	*Purchase Ledger Control*

NOTE: The number of lines shown in (a) and (b) above does NOT necessarily correspond with the number of accounts required.

2.9   Comart Supplies Ltd recently purchased from Ace Imports Ltd 10 printers originally priced at £200 each. A 10% trade discount was negotiated together with a 5% cash discount if payment was made within 14 days. Calculate the following:

   (a)   The total of the trade discount.

   £ 200.00

   (b)   The total of the cash discount.

   £ 90.00

   (c)   The total of the VAT.

   £ 299.25

2.10   Some office equipment has been ordered from a supplier who has requested that payment should be made before the equipment has been delivered and before invoicing. You understand that a cheque can be issued against a properly completed cheque requisition form.

   What system of control should exist to ensure that cheques are only issued in such circumstances for valid items of expenditure?

   Proforma Invoice. Make sure you don't pay invoice again

   when you receive it.

2.11   In taking out the bank loan referred to earlier, the company was required by the bank to give a mortgage over its premises.

   (a)   In the mortgagor/mortgagee relationship described, which party is the mortgagor?

   Comart Supplies Ltd/The bank

   (b)   Explain briefly the reason why the bank would normally ask for the mortgage.

   For security. If Comart Supplies failed to pay off the

   bank loan, the bank could take possession over the premises

2.12   Give TWO reasons why a business should avoid settling its debts by sending cash through the post.

   1) Security, no guarantee cash will reach the right person.

   2) Person receiving cash would prefer a cheque as it is
   easier to deal with than cash, takes less time.
   3) evidence of receipt.

2.13 Would the following errors cause a difference to occur between the balance of the creditors control account and the total of the balances in the purchases ledger?

(a) A creditor's account has been balanced off incorrectly.

Yes/No

(b) An invoice for £37 has been entered into the purchases day book as £39.

Yes/No

(c) An invoice has, in error, been omitted from the purchases day book.

Yes/No

2.14 Wendy Roberts, one of Comart Supplies Ltd's sales staff, offers to sell a second-hand colour printer to Robert Ford for £175. Robert wants time to think about it and Wendy tells him that she will leave the offer open until the end of the day. At 2.00 p.m. Robert calls back to say that is willing to buy the printer for £160. At 3.00 p.m. Wendy sells the printer to Caroline Brown for £175 and arranges delivery for the following day. At 4.30 p.m. Robert returns and tells Wendy that he is now willing to buy the printer for £175.

(a) Can Robert claim that he has a contract with the company and insist that the printer is sold to him?

Yes/No

(b) Briefly explain the reason for your answer.

Robert made a counter-offer by offering less than £175 so Wendy was within her rights to reject her offer.

2.15 Wendy Roberts checks her bank statement and realises that she only has £120 left in her account with bills to pay totalling £200. Her salary is due in two weeks time and she does not foresee similar problems occurring again in the near future. Which bank service would seem the most appropriate to meet her needs?

Bank overdraft/Bank loan

2.16 Should the total of the VAT column in a petty cash book be debited or credited to the VAT account?

Debited/Credited

2.17 On 15 May, Comart Supplies Ltd received some new software from County Computers Ltd. A letter which was enclosed acknowledged that the software had not been ordered and pointed out that it was being offered at a special price of £265. The letter also stated that unless County Computers Ltd had heard from Comart Supplies Ltd within 10 days it would be assumed that the purchase was to be concluded and an invoice would be issued. By 25 May Comart Supplies Ltd had not responded to the letter.

(a) Does a contract to purchase the software exist between the two companies?

~~Yes~~/No

(b) Briefly explain the reason for your answer.

Silence does not constitute acceptance
Comart Supplies Ltd did not accept the offer & County Computers Ltd imposed conditions. Acceptance must also be unconditional.

2.18 An advice note is a document sent to a customer advising the customer or acknowledging that an order has been received. Advice of despatch

~~True~~/False

False

2.19 Give two advantages of using a computerised accounting system.

a) More accurate method of recording business transactions

b) More efficient & quicker once the system is set up & running smoothly.

c) hold more information.

2.20 A manufacturer sells a product to a wholesaler for £200 plus VAT of £35. The wholesaler sells the same product to a retailer for £280 plus VAT of £49. The retailer then sells the product to a customer for £320 plus VAT of £56. What is the total amount of VAT collectable by HM Customs & Excise relating to the product?

£ 56

You do not add up all the separate amounts, e.g 35 + 49 + 56

CENTRAL ASSESSMENT TASKS – SUMMIT GLAZING LIMITED

3

Communication exercises relating to these tasks may be found on page 236

INTRODUCTION

The tasks and questions are based on the transactions of Summit Glazing Limited. The company provides a glazing service to commercial and domestic customers. It also constructs conservatories and installs replacement windows which are bought in from specialist manufacturers.

The Managing Director is Chris Cooper and Mary Owen is the Accountant/Company Secretary. You are employed as an Accounting Technician to assist Mary Owen.

DATA

The following transactions all occurred on 1 December 1995 and have yet to be entered into the ledger system. VAT has been calculated at the rate of 17.5%.

SALES INVOICES ISSUED

	Total	VAT	Net
	£	£	£
G C J Builders Ltd	8,460	1,260	7,200
Acorn Housing Association	£6,063	903	5,160
Cordington Plc	2,021	301	1,720
James Building Services	799	119	680
	17,343	2,583	14,760

PURCHASES INVOICES RECEIVED

	Total	VAT	Net
	£	£	£
Georgian Conservatories	705	105	600
Diamond Glass Ltd	2,115	315	1,800
Russell Timber Supplies	423	63	360
Elite Windows	1,269	189	1,080
	4,512	672	3,840

CREDIT NOTE RECEIVED

	Total	VAT	Net
	£	£	£
Diamond Glass Ltd	47	7	40

CASH SALES

	Total	VAT	Net
	£	£	£
Cheques	141	21	120
Notes and coins	188	28	160
	329	49	280

CHEQUE RECEIVED

	£
Acorn Housing Association	6,200

CHEQUES ISSUED

	£	
Georgian Conservatories	27,195	(Full settlement of a debt of £27,750)
Elite Windows	13,995	

JOURNAL ENTRY

	Debit	Credit
	£	£
Motor expenses	340	
Motor vehicles		340

Correction of error: Cost of repairs on delivery van debited in error to the motor vehicles account.

ACCOUNT BALANCES

The following balances are available to you at the start of the day on 1 December 1995:

	£
Purchases	897,953
Sales	1,138,325
Purchase returns	4,280
Bank (debit balance)	22,723
Bank charges	1,567
VAT (credit balance)	8,136
Discounts allowed	6,340
Discounts received	2,892

	£
Sales ledger control (debtors)	85,995 ✓
Purchase ledger control (creditors)	78,237 ✓
Wages	282,500
Rent and rates	16,225
Electricity	4,106
Telephone	1,852
Motor expenses	6,857 ✓
Insurance	5,935
Sundry expenses	2,734
Motor vehicles	56,900 ✓
Machinery & equipment	15,120
Sundry creditors	11,867
Stocks	48,930
Capital	212,000

PROCESSING EXERCISE

COMPLETE ALL THE FOLLOWING TASKS

Task 1   Enter the opening balances into the following accounts:

>   Bank (cash book)
>   Sales ledger control (debtors)
>   Purchase ledger control (creditors)
>   Purchases
>   Sales
>   VAT
>   Purchase returns
>   Discounts received
>   Motor vehicles
>   Motor expenses

These accounts can be found on the pages that follow.

Task 2   Using the data shown on pages 192 - 194, enter all the transactions into the accounts in Task 1.

Task 3   Balance the cash book on page 198 and total the discount and VAT columns, transferring the totals to the appropriate accounts.

Task 4   Balance all the remaining accounts in which you have made entries.

Note: You are not required to update any accounts other than those shown in Task 1.

Task 5   Complete the list of balances on page 199 by inserting the figure for each account in either the debit column or the credit column as appropriate. Total the two columns. The two totals should be the same. If they do not agree, try to trace and correct any errors you have made within the time available. If you are still unable to make the totals balance, leave the work incomplete.

GENERAL LEDGER

Dr   Cr

Sales ledger control account

Date	Details	Amount	Date	Details	Amount
		£			£

Dr   Cr

Purchase ledger control account

Date	Details	Amount	Date	Details	Amount
		£			£

Dr   Cr

Purchases

Date	Details	Amount	Date	Details	Amount
		£			£

Sales

Dr					Cr
Date	Details	Amount	Date	Details	Amount
		£			£

VAT

Dr					Cr
Date	Details	Amount	Date	Details	Amount
		£			£

Purchases returns

Dr					Cr
Date	Details	Amount	Date	Details	Amount
		£			£

Dr   **Discounts received**   Cr

Date	Details	Amount	Date	Details	Amount
		£			£

Dr   **Motor vehicles**   Cr

Date	Details	Amount	Date	Details	Amount
		£			£

Dr   **Motor expenses**   Cr

Date	Details	Amount	Date	Details	Amount
		£			£

CASH BOOK

Date	Details	Discount allowed £	VAT £	Cash £	Bank £

Date	Details	Discount received £	VAT £	Cash £	Bank £

LIST OF UPDATED BALANCES:

	Debit balances £	Credit balances £
Purchases		
Sales		
Purchase returns		
Bank		
Bank charges		
Cash		
VAT		
Discounts allowed		
Discounts received		
Sales ledger control (debtors)		
Purchase ledger control (creditors)		
Wages		
Rent & rates		
Electricity		
Telephone		
Motor expenses		
Insurance		
Sundry expenses		
Motor vehicles		
Machinery & equipment		
Sundry creditors		
Stocks		
Capital		
TOTALS		

SHORT ANSWER QUESTIONS

Using, where appropriate, the information given in the Processing Exercise, write on the dotted lines or circle the correct answer. Note that the date today is 1 December 1995.

National Bank plc	*27 November 1994*
82 Market Street Swindon	
Pay *Summit Glazing Limited*	
Five hundred and four pounds	**£ 540.00**
ACCOUNT PAYEE	C Lawton

3.1 The above cheque has been received from a customer. Give two reasons why it would not be accepted for payment if it was presented to National Bank Plc.

(a) Stale, out of date over 6 months old

(b) Not signed

3.2 What book-keeping entries are required in the general ledger to record a dishonoured cheque which has been received from a customer and paid into Summit Glazing's bank account?

(a) Debit Sales Account   Debtors Ledger Control

(b) Credit Bank Account

3.3 Summit Glazing Ltd is planning to purchase a new van. Would the following items be capital or revenue expenditure?

(a) The purchase price of the van.

Capital/Revenue

(b) Modification work to the side of the van to allow the external carriage of sheets of glass.

Capital/Revenue

(c) Motor insurance for the van.

Capital/Revenue

3.4   Which accounts are contained in the purchase ledger?

Individual Creditors; Purchase Returns; Discount Received

3.5   Summit Glazing received an enquiry from Stanhope Builders to purchase a Viceroy conservatory. A quotation was sent out offering to supply a Viceroy for £5,600. The next day Mary Owen realised a mistake had been made as the price quoted should have been £6,500. Mary immediately wrote to Stanhope Builders informing them that the quoted price was incorrect and that the conservatory could not therefore be supplied as offered. The following day Karl Hope from Stanhope Builders telephoned to say that although he had received Mary's letter he wanted to accept the original offer, insisting that the conservatory should be supplied for £5,600.

   (a)   Does a valid contract exist between Summit Glazing and Stanhope Builders?

   Yes/No

   (b)   Explain briefly the reason for your answer.

   Offer was revised before acceptance was made

3.6   Cash discounts are only available to customers who pay immediately in cash.

   True/False

3.7   Complete the following sentences by inserting the name of the appropriate document.

   (a)   Summit Glazing sends out a ......Statement...... to each credit customer on a monthly basis which summarises the transactions that have taken place and shows the amount owed by the customer.

   (b)   Summit Glazing sends out a ......Credit Note...... to a credit customer in order to correct an error where the customer has been overcharged by an invoice.

   (c)   Summit Glazing sends out a ......Remittance Advice...... with a payment to a supplier to indicate which invoices are being paid.

3.8   Classify the following ledger accounts according to whether they represent asset/liability/expense or revenue.

   (a)   Insurance

   Asset/liability/expense/revenue

   (b)   Stock

   Asset/liability/expense/revenue

(c)   Discounts received

Asset/liability/expense/(revenue)

(d)   Bank overdraft

Asset/(liability)/expense/revenue

3.9   During the quarter ended 31 October 1995 sales amounted to £731,555 inclusive of VAT at 17.5%. On the 31 October the credit balance on the VAT account was £47,600. Calculate the value of vatable purchases made during the quarter inclusive of VAT.

Note: Your answer should include detailed workings.

VAT ACCOUNT

Purchases	61,355	Sales	108,955	
Bal C/D	47,600			
	108,955		108,955	
		Bal B/D	47,600	

£731,555 × 17.5 ÷ 117.5 = £108,955

Vat on Purchases £61,355 × 1.175
                        0.175

= £411,955

3.10   When using a computer to process accounting data there are two main systems which can be adopted.

(a)   The system where documents or transactions for a period are grouped and processed together is known as .....Batched........... processing.

(b)   The system where documents or transactions are input as they occur is known as ....Daily...............processing.
       On-line or real time

3.11   On 18 November a customer, Mr Green, had a double glazed replacement window fitted by Summit Glazing. He telephoned the next day complaining that one of the toplights would not open. The Summit Glazing employee who inspected the window said it appeared to be a manufacturing fault and advised Mr Green to contact the manufacturer to have the fault corrected.

(a)   Was the employee legally justified in advising Mr Green to contact the manufacturer?

Yes/No

(b)   Explain briefly the reason for your answer.

Summit supplied the window & it is their responsibility to sort out the problem.

3.12   List three checks that should be made when accepting a credit card from a customer in payment for goods.

(i)   Credit limit is not exceeded

(ii)   Signature is the same on card & voucher

(iii) Check expiry date has not run out

3.13 Give one reason for maintaining a sales ledger (debtors) control account.

Immediate up to date information of total debtors

3.14 What book-keeping entries would be necessary to record a cash refund of £94 (inclusive of VAT) to a customer?

Debit	Amount £	Credit	Amount £
VAT	*14.00*	*Customer* *Cash*	*94.00* *80.00*

3.15 Would the following errors cause a difference between the balance of the purchase ledger (creditors) control account and the total of the balances in the purchase ledger?

(a)   The purchase day book was overcast by £10.

~~Yes~~/No   *Yes*

(b)   The value of a purchase invoice was credited to the account of ACL Ltd instead of A C Lead Ltd.

Yes/~~No~~

(c)   An invoice for £47 was recorded in the purchase day book as £74.

Yes/~~No~~

3.16 Summit Glazing operates an imprest petty cash system. The imprest amount is £150.00. At the end of the period the totals of the four analysis columns in the petty cash book were as follows:

Column 1 £23.12; Column 2 £6.74; Column 3 £12.90; Column 4 £28.50

How much cash is required to restore the imprest amount? £ *71.26*

3.17 Summit Glazing has an overdraft facility of £20,000. When Summit Glazing's current account is overdrawn is the bank a debtor or creditor in Summit Glazing's accounts?

Debtor/~~Creditor~~

3.18 Give two uses of the Journal as a book of original entry.

(i)   *Correcting Errors*

(ii) *Purchase & sale of fixed assets on credit*

3.19 What does it mean if goods are sold "carriage paid"?

Price of the goods includes delivery

3.20 Summit Glazing is considering transferring some of its records to microfiche. Give one advantage that microfiche has over paper records.

Able to store more information which takes up less space

CENTRAL ASSESSMENT TASKS – BLOOMERS LIMITED

4

Communication exercises relating to these tasks may be found on page 239

INTRODUCTION

The tasks and questions are based on the transactions of Bloomers Limited. The company operates a chain of flower shops. In addition to the sales made in its shops, the company also has several contracts with local hotels to supply and maintain flower displays.

The Managing Director is Alison Pallister and Paul Lazenby is the Accountant. You are employed as an Accounting Technician to assist Paul Lazenby.

DATA

The following transactions all occurred on 1 June 1996 and have yet to be entered into the ledger system. VAT has been calculated at the rate of 17.5%.

A bank statement was received on 1 June.

SALES INVOICES ISSUED

	Total £	VAT £	Net £
York Hotels Ltd	846	126	720
Deluxe Hotels Plc	235	35	200
Prime Hotels Ltd	376	56	320
Deluxe Hotels Plc	564	84	480
	2,021	301	1,720

PURCHASES INVOICES RECEIVED

	Total £	VAT £	Net £	Goods for resale £	Heating & lighting £
Exotic Blooms Ltd	1,269	189	1,080	1,080	
Island Flowers Co	4,230	630	3,600	3,600	
Floristry Supplies Ltd	470	70	400	400	
Yorkshire Electricity Plc	423	63	360		360
	6,392	952	5,440	5,080	360

CREDIT NOTE ISSUED

	Total	VAT	Net
	£	£	£
Deluxe Hotels Plc	94	14	80

CREDIT NOTE RECEIVED

	Total	VAT	Net
	£	£	£
Exotic Blooms Ltd	235	35	200

JOURNAL ENTRIES

	Debit	Credit
	£	£
Equipment	210	
Heating and lighting		210
(Heater installed - incorrectly debited to heating and lighting account)		
Yorkshire Hotels Plc	141	
York Hotels Ltd		141
(Correction of misposting of sales invoice in the sales ledger)		

ACCOUNT BALANCES

The following balances are available to you at the start of the day on 1 June 1996:

	£
Sales ledger (debtors) control	13,489
Purchase ledger (creditors) control	7,688
Sales	291,876
Purchases	126,934
VAT (credit balance)	6,920
Heating and lighting	11,962
Customers:	
York Hotels Ltd	1,081
Deluxe Hotels Plc	2,256
Prime Hotels Ltd	1,739
Other customers	8,413

The following bank statement was received on 1 June 1996:

NORTHERN BANK PLC   **Statement of Account**
120 Lower High Street
York
TK12 5SW

Account: Bloomers Limited
Account no 11598234   Statement no 107   Statement date 31 May 1996

Date	Details	Withdrawals	Deposits	Balance
1996		£	£	£
27 May	Balance brought forward			2,100.00 Cr
28 May	Credit		4,000.00	6,100.00 Cr
29 May	Bank charges	70.00		6,030.00 Cr
30 May	Credit		2,120.00	8,150.00 Cr
31 May	BGC Prime Hotels Ltd		650.00	8,800.00 Cr
31 May	Cheque 1005682	1,860.00		6,940.00 Cr

SO Standing Order **DD** Direct Debit **TR** Transfer **BGC** Bank giro credit **BACS** Automated transfer

---

PROCESSING EXERCISE

COMPLETE ALL THE FOLLOWING TASKS

Task 1   Enter the opening balances into the following accounts:
   Sales ledger (debtors) control
   Purchase ledger (creditors) control
   Sales
   Purchases
   VAT
   Heating & lighting
   York Hotels Ltd
   Deluxe Hotels Plc
   Prime Hotels Ltd

   These accounts can be found on pages 207 to 209

Task 2   Using the data shown on pages 204 and 205, enter all the relevant transactions into the accounts listed in Task 1.

Task 3   Balance off all the accounts, clearly showing the balances carried down.

Task 4   Update the cash book on page 210, using appropriate information taken from the bank statement. Balance off the bank account, clearly showing the balance carried down.

Task 5   Prepare a bank reconciliation statement as at 1 June 1996, using page 210.

GENERAL LEDGER

Dr   **Sales ledger control account**   Cr

Date	Details	Amount	Date	Details	Amount
		£			£

Dr   **Purchase ledger control account**   Cr

Date	Details	Amount	Date	Details	Amount
		£			£

Dr   **Sales**   Cr

Date	Details	Amount	Date	Details	Amount
		£			£

Dr   **Purchases**   Cr

Date	Details	Amount	Date	Details	Amount
		£			£

Dr   **VAT**   Cr

Date	Details	Amount	Date	Details	Amount
		£			£

Dr   **Heating & lighting**   Cr

Date	Details	Amount	Date	Details	Amount
		£			£

SALES LEDGER

Dr   **York Hotels Ltd**   Cr

Date	Details	Amount	Date	Details	Amount
		£			£

Dr   **Deluxe Hotels PLC**   Cr

Date	Details	Amount	Date	Details	Amount
		£			£

Dr   **Prime Hotels Ltd**   Cr

Date	Details	Amount	Date	Details	Amount
		£			£

Cash Book (bank columns only)

		£			£
May 27	Balance b/d	2,100	May 27	Flora (UK) Ltd	1,860
May 27	Cash sales	4,000	May 29	STD Supplies Ltd	542
May 29	Cash sales	2,120	May 30	Business rates	4,320
May 31	Cash sales				

BLOOMERS LTD

Bank Reconciliation Statement as at 1 June 1996

SHORT ANSWER QUESTIONS

Using, where appropriate, the information given in the Processing Exercise, write on the dotted lines or circle the correct answer.

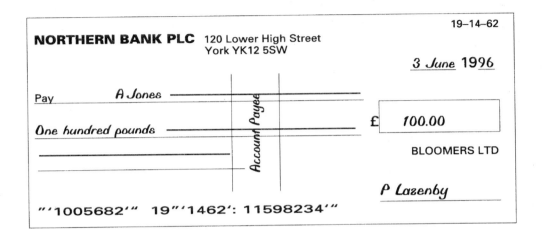

NORTHERN BANK PLC   120 Lower High Street
York YK12 5SW

19–14–62

3 June 1996

Pay   A Jones

One hundred pounds

Account Payee

£   100.00

BLOOMERS LTD

P Lazenby

"'1005682'" 19"'1462': 11598234'"

4.1   Briefly explain the effect of the crossing on the above cheque.

.... The cheque must be paid into A Jones Account ....

....

4.2   Referring to the cheque given in question 4.1, give the name of:

(a)   the drawer ...Bloomers Ltd.....

(b)   the drawee ...Northern Bank Plc

(c)   the payee ...A Jones...

4.3   Name **three** primary records used for listing transactions before they are posted to the ledger accounts.

(a)   Sales Day Book.

(b)   Purchases Day Book

(c)   Sales Returns Day Book

4.4   If capital expenditure is treated as revenue expenditure, the total of expenses for the period will be

(too high)/too low/unaffected

4.5   Bloomers Ltd purchases 40 glass crystal vases for £7.50 each plus VAT. The vases are then all sold to a hotel gift shop for £517 inclusive of VAT. How much is owed by Bloomers to HM Customs and Excise in respect of the vases?

Input Vat - Output Vat

Note: Your answer should include detailed workings.

517 x 17.5 ÷ 117.5 = £77 Vat
40 @ £7.50 = £300   52.50 vat input) difference between the
sold for   517   77.00 output) two £24.50.

4.6   Gift Box is both a supplier to and a customer of Bloomers Ltd. It has been agreed that a debt of £75 owing to Gift Box is to be set-off against the balance of £300 owed by Gift Box.

What entries would be required in the general ledger to record this set-off?

Debit	Amount	Credit	Amount
Creditors Control	75.00	Debtors Control	75.00

4.7   List **three** checks that should be carried out, in respect of the card, when a cheque supported by a cheque guarantee card is received from a customer.

(a)   Signature should be the same on the card and the cheque.

(b)   Check the number is the same on the card and the cheque.

(c)   Check the guarantee limit. The cheque should not be greater than the card limit.

4.8   An arrangement of dried flowers has been displayed with a £5 price ticket. A customer wanting to purchase the arrangement was told that an incorrect price ticket had been used and that the price was in fact £25.

(a)   Can the customer insist on purchasing the arrangement for £5?

   Yes/~~No~~

(b)   Explain briefly the reason for your answer

The £ price ticket is only an invitation to treat, an invitation for the customer to make an agreement to purchase the flowers for the price indicated at the checkout.

4.9   A remittance advice is a document sent by a supplier to a customer to advise the customer that goods ordered have been dispatched to the customer.

True/False

4.10   Bloomers Ltd has recently purchased a range of decorative ribbons from Sundries Galore Ltd. The total list price of the ribbons was £340 exclusive of VAT, but Sundries Galore gave Bloomers a trade discount of 20% and, in addition, a cash discount of 5% if payment was made within 7 days.

Calculate the following:

(a)   The value of the trade discount

£ 68.00

(b)   The value of the cash discount available

£ 13.60

(c)   The value of VAT charged in respect of this purchase

£ 45.22

4.11   Should the total of the discounts allowed column in the cash book be debited or credited to the discounts allowed account?

Debited/Credited

4.12   What word is used to describe a computerised accounting system which automatically updates all the records involved in a financial transaction from one computer entry?

Integrated   Sage

4.13   Bloomers has agreed to make regular monthly payments to Apollo Communications plc. The amount of the payment varies from month to month. Which service provided by the banks would appear to be most appropriate for these payments?

Direct Debit

4.14   Bloomers Ltd has been asked to give a quotation for supplying flowers for an international conference, which is to be organised by CMP plc. The quotation was sent by post on 22 May 1996 and received by CMP plc the next day. CMP plc posted a letter accepting Bloomer's quotation on 29 May 1996. This letter was received by Bloomers on 30 May 1996.,

(a)   On which date was the contract made?

(I)   23 May 1996

(ii)   29 May 1996

(iii)   30 May 1996

(b)   Explain briefly the reason for your answer

Due to the Postal Rule a contract is formed when a customer posts the letter accepting Bloomers quotation

4.15   Would the following accounts be found in the general ledger, the purchase ledger or the sales ledger?

(a)   Exotic Blooms Ltd (a credit supplier) ...Purchase ledger...

(b)   Salaries and wages ...General ledger...

(c)   Motor vehicles ...General ledger...

cost to buy   *cost to you of sending out*

4.16   Carriage inwards and carriage outwards are both expense accounts:

True/False

4.17   Why is it important to keep bad debts to a minimum?

...Because they are a cost to the business. If you allow customers to run up bad debts you could go bankrupt as you will be short of working capital...

4.18   Give two different circumstances which would require a credit note to be issued.

(i)   ...Wrong goods have been sent...

(ii)   ...Faulty goods have been sent...

4.19   What book-keeping entries would be required in the general ledger to correct the following error?

A credit note for £160 plus £28 VAT issued to a customer has been treated as if it were a credit note received.

Debit	Amount	Credit	Amount
	£		£
Purchase Returns	160.00	Debtors *cannot*	186.00
Sales Returns	160.00		
VAT	28.00		
VAT	28.00		

4.20   A debit card allows a customer to use funds held in her bank account to make a payment without the need to issue a cheque.

True/False

CENTRAL ASSESSMENT TASKS – MMS TEXTILES LIMITED

5

Communication exercises relating to these tasks may be found on page 241

INTRODUCTION

MMS Textiles Limited is a business making curtains and other home furnishing items, which it retails through the market stalls it operates. The company also supplies other retail businesses. The manufacturing process takes place in a factory on the Brooklands industrial estate. The Managing Director is Mariam Saleem and you are an accounting technician employed by the firm to maintain the accounting system.

DATA

The following transactions all occurred on 1 December 1996 and have not yet been entered into the ledger system. VAT has been calculated at the rate of 17.5%.

PURCHASE INVOICES RECEIVED

	Total	VAT	Net	Goods for resale	Rent	Insurance
	£	£	£	£	£	£
Timbrell Fabrics Ltd	1,692	252	1,440	1,440		
Walsall MBC	240		240		240	
PNB Supplies & Sundries Ltd	470	70	400	400		
Guardian Insurance Plc	564		564			564
Mona Fabrics Ltd	752	112	640	640		
	3,718	434	3,284	2,480	240	564

CREDIT NOTES RECEIVED

	Total	VAT	Net
	£	£	£
Mona Fabrics Ltd	188	28	160
PNB Supplies & Sundries Ltd	47	7	40
	235	35	200

CHEQUES PAID

	£	
Mona Fabrics Ltd	2,185	In full settlement of an invoice for £2,300
Timbrell Fabrics Ltd	376	

BALANCES

The following balances are available to you at the start of the day on 1 December 1996:

	£
Purchases	260,890
Purchase ledger control	34,960
VAT (Credit balance)	17,785
Purchase returns	572
Discounts received	2,867
Rent	15,450
Insurance	3,678
Postage	435
Stationery	675
Cleaning	238
Sundry expenses	724

PROCESSING EXERCISE

Task 1   Enter the opening balances listed above into the following accounts, which are provided on pages 218 to 221.

Purchases
Purchase ledger control
VAT
Purchase returns
Discounts received
Rent
Insurance
Postage
Stationery
Cleaning
Sundry expenses

Task 2   Using the data shown earlier, enter all the transactions into the accounts listed in Task 1.

Task 3   Write up the petty cash book shown on page 222:
- recording the petty cash vouchers from page 217
- balancing the petty cash book
- restoring the imprest
- transferring the totals to the appropriate general ledger accounts

Note: the cost of stationery on voucher no. 768 includes VAT charged at the rate of 17.5%. All the other petty cash items are either exempt or zero rated.

Task 4   Balance off all the general ledger accounts provided, clearly showing the balances carried down.

PETTY CASH

The following petty cash vouchers have been made out in respect of petty cash paid out on 1 December 1996:

PETTY CASH VOUCHER	No *763*	
Date *1 December 1996*		
	£	p
Tea, coffee and milk	4	32
	4	32
Signature *J Jones* Authorised *S Smith*		

PETTY CASH VOUCHER	No *764*	
Date *1 December 1996*		
	£	p
Stamps	5	00
	5	00
Signature *J Jones* Authorised *S Smith*		

PETTY CASH VOUCHER	No *765*	
Date *1 December 1996*		
	£	p
Window cleaning	10	80
	10	80
Signature *R Singh* Authorised *S Smith*		

PETTY CASH VOUCHER	No *766*	
Date *1 December 1996*		
	£	p
Parcel postage	4	70
Recorded delivery	1	30
	6	00
Signature *J Jones* Authorised *S Smith*		

PETTY CASH VOUCHER	No *767*	
Date *1 December 1996*		
	£	p
Bus fare	1	50
	1	50
Signature *J Jones* Authorised *S Smith*		

PETTY CASH VOUCHER	No *768*	
Date *1 December 1996*		
	£	p
A4 envelopes	2	35
Photocopy paper	4	70
	7	05
Signature *M Gono* Authorised *S Smith*		

GENERAL LEDGER

Dr   **Purchases**   Cr

Date	Details	Amount	Date	Details	Amount
		£			£

Dr   **Purchase ledger control account**   Cr

Date	Details	Amount	Date	Details	Amount
		£			£

Dr   **VAT**   Cr

Date	Details	Amount	Date	Details	Amount
		£			£

Purchases returns

Dr | | | Cr

Date	Details	Amount £	Date	Details	Amount £

Discounts received

Dr | | | Cr

Date	Details	Amount £	Date	Details	Amount £

Rent

Dr | | | Cr

Date	Details	Amount £	Date	Details	Amount £

Dr   **Insurance**   Cr

Date	Details	Amount	Date	Details	Amount
		£			£

Dr   **Postage**   Cr

Date	Details	Amount	Date	Details	Amount
		£			£

Dr   **Stationery**   Cr

Date	Details	Amount	Date	Details	Amount
		£			£

Cleaning

Dr | | | | | Cr

Date	Details	Amount	Date	Details	Amount
		£			£

Sundry expenses

Dr | | | | | Cr

Date	Details	Amount	Date	Details	Amount
		£			£

PETTY CASH BOOK

Receipts	Date	Details	Voucher No.	Payment	VAT	Postage	Stationery	Cleaning	Sundry exp.
							Analysis columns		
£					£	£	£	£	£
40.00	1996 Dec 1	*Balance (imprest) b/d*							

SHORT ANSWER QUESTIONS

Using, where appropriate, the information given in the Processing Exercise, write on the dotted line or circle the correct answer.

5.1   MMS Textiles Ltd banks at the Moxley branch of the Norwest Bank, sort code no. 36-24-41, and its account number is 479836806.

Fill in the paying-in slip and counterfoil given below to bank the cash takings on 1 December which are as follows:

Four	£50 notes
Twenty-three	£20 notes
Thirty-two	£10 notes
Seven	£5 notes
Eight	50 pence coins
Twelve	10 pence coins

Date 1 12 96

Credit

£50 Notes	200	00
£20 Notes	460	00
£10 Notes	320	00
£5 Notes	35	00
£1	—	
50p	4	00
20p	1	20
10p, 5p		
Bronze		
Total cash	1,020	20
Cheques etc. see over		
£	1,020	20

Date 1 12 96

Cashier's stamp and initials

bank giro credit

Code no 36 — 24 — 41

Bank Norwest Bank

Branch Moxley

Credit MMS Textiles Ltd

Account no 47983806

Paid in by Accounting Technician

Number of cheques

0

£50 Notes	200	00
£20 Notes	460	00
£10 Notes	320	00
£5 Notes	35	00
£1		
50p	4	00
20p	1	20
10p, 5p		
Bronze		
Total cash	1,020	20
Cheques etc. see over		
£	1,020	20

5.2   Norwest Bank has arranged the insurance of all the company's assets. In this transaction what is the banker/customer relationship?

Principal and agent/Mortgagor and mortgagee

5.3   Would a direct debit paid by the Norwest Bank out of MMS Textiles' bank account appear in the MMS Textiles cash book as a debit or credit entry?

Debit/Credit

5.4 MMS Textiles Ltd is a VAT registered firm. Should they charge VAT on goods supplied to a customer who is not VAT registered?

Yes/No

5.5 For what period of time must VAT records be retained?

6 months/6 years

5.6 The following invoice received by MMS Textiles has been passed to you for checking. Give TWO reasons why it CANNOT be passed for payment.

(a) 20 spools of polyester thread @ 5.80 should be £116.00

(b) There is no date on it

INVOICE   No *12426*

Superior Sundries Ltd   Tel: 0121 559 3442
12–14 Dawley Road
BIRMINGHAM BM8 2JR   VAT Reg No. 643 112211

Date/Tax Point:

Quantity	Description	Unit Price £ p	Total Amount £ p
20	Spools polyester thread	5 80	126 00
10	Rolls of curtain tape	23 50	235 00
5	Boxes of curtain hooks	7 60	38 00
	Total excluding VAT		399 00
	VAT @ 17.5%		69 82
	Total due		468 82

Terms: 30 days net
Carriage paid

Registered Office: 12–14 Dawley Road, Birmingham BM8 2JR.
Registered Number 4524634

5.7 MMS Textiles Ltd has recently sent a quotation to a local builder, Tall Trees Construction Plc, to supply and fit curtains for a new house. Tall Trees Construction Plc has replied accepting the quotation provided that all the curtains are installed by 20 December 1996.

    (a) Does a contract exist at this stage?

       Yes/No

    (b) Explain briefly the reason for your answer.

       The acceptance has been conditional. Tall trees Construction Plc have made a counter-offer by introducing a new term.

5.8 Complete the following sentences:

    (a) An Advice Note is sent to the buyer before the goods are delivered to inform that the goods will be despatched shortly.

    (b) A Delivery Note is packed with goods so that the buyer can check that all the items listed have been received.

    (c) An Invoice is sent by the seller to the buyer of goods to advise how much is owed for the goods supplied.

5.9 Classify the following ledger accounts according to whether they represent asset, liability, expense or revenue.

    (a) Discounts allowed

       Asset/liability/expense/revenue

    (b) Bank loan

       Asset/liability/expense/revenue

    (c) Commission received

       Asset/liability/expense/revenue   X   3/4

    (d) Carriage inwards

       Asset/liability/expense/revenue

5.10 All the sales, including cash sales, are recorded in the sales ledger control account.

    True/False   only credit sales

5.11 What entries are required in the GENERAL LEDGER to write off a bad debt of £188, inclusive of VAT at 17.5%? The VAT can be reclaimed.

Debit	Amount (£)	Credit	Amount (£)
Bad debts written off	160	Debtors Control a/c	188
VAT	28		

5.12   The cash book is a book of primary record.

  True/False

5.13   At present MMS Textiles Ltd maintains a manual accounting system but Mariam Saleem is considering installing a computerised system. Give THREE advantages of storing information on computer.

  (a)   Takes up less space ie discs ✓

  (b)   Quicker as amounts are automatically transferred to other dcs.

  (c)   Less errors.

5.14   Would the following errors cause a difference to occur between the balance on the purchase ledger control account and the total of the balances in the purchase ledger?

  (a)   The purchases day book has been overcast by £50.

  Yes/No ✗

  (b)   A purchase for £65 has been debited to the supplier's account.

  Yes/No

  2/3

  (c)   A purchase invoice received from Tapes and Braids Ltd has been credited to the account of Tapes and Tassels Ltd.

  Yes/No

5.15   Mariam Saleem has promised to make a set of curtains free of charge for a regular customer, Jane Walker. After three months the curtains have not been made and Jane has phoned Mariam and demanded that the curtains be made as promised.

  (a)   Can Jane legally insist that the curtains are made as promised?

  Yes/No ✗

  (b)   Briefly explain the reason for your answer.   ✗ No consideration

  verbal

  A contract has been formed when Mariam Saleem promised to make the curtains. This is legally binding.

5.16   What does it mean if goods are sold COD?

  Cash on Delivery

5.17 List TWO classification methods for filing documents and files.

(a) Alphabetical

(b) Numerical

5.18 At present MMS Textiles Ltd does not accept credit card payment but Mariam is considering introducing a credit card facility.

(a) Give one disadvantage to the retailer of accepting credit card payments.

MMS Textiles Ltd pays a percentage of each transaction amount for the use of the credit card facility

(b) In the seller's books of account a credit card sale is treated as a cash transaction.

True/False

5.19 Give THREE reasons why the balance shown on MMS Textiles' bank statement may not agree with the balance on its bank account in the cash book.

(a) Unpresented Cheques

(b) Outstanding lodgements

(c) Standing Order BACS

5.20 On 1 December 1996 the account of Berg Interiors Ltd, in the sales ledger, is as follows:

Berg Interiors Ltd

1996		£	1996		£
Oct 1	Balance b/d	1,420	Oct 4	Bank	750
Oct 29	Sales	640			
Nov 8	Sales	325			
Nov 22	Sales	860			

Complete the following age analysis for this customer:

	Up to 1 month	Up to 2 months	Over 2 months
Age analysis as at 1 December 1996	1,185	1,370	670

640

CENTRAL ASSESSMENT COMMUNICATION TASKS – CHANG FASHIONS LIMITED

these tasks are linked to the processing tasks which start on page 168

TASK 1

You have been asked to help resolve a problem concerning one of Chang Fashion Ltd's suppliers. The following details have been provided:

12 October 1994, purchase order P00234 sent to Ace Imports Ltd.

Order for two boxes of jeans.

Delivery 26 October. One box contains cotton trousers instead of jeans (trousers not ordered).

Telephone calls made by Mary Chang to Mr Brian Moody at Ace Imports Ltd on 27 October. Brian Moody promises to deliver a replacement box and take away the trousers within 14 days.

Invoice dated 16 November received from Ace Imports Ltd on 18 November. Invoice is for two boxes of jeans at £764.92 each and refers to order P00234.

To date no further action from Ace Imports Ltd.

Using the headed paper on the next page, draft a letter to Brian Moody at Ace Imports Ltd, 165 Dell Trading Estate, Southampton SO10 4EP. The letter, which is to be dated 2 December 1994, is to be signed by Rahul Divan and should include the following:

(a)   Details of the original error.

(b)   The arrangements made to correct the error.

(c)   A request for the exchange of products to take place immediately.

(d)   A request for early notification and the issue of a credit note if (c) is not possible.

Chang Fashions Ltd
142 Regent Court
London
WE4 1NN
Tel: 0181 803 6712

Chang Fashions Ltd. Registered Office: 142 Regent Court, London WE4 1NN
Registered in England, number 5469971

CHANG FASHIONS – TASK 2

The following letter has been received:

STAR LINE INSURANCE LTD
23 Vicarage Road
Watford
HE9 0BU
Tel: 01293 76824

30 November 1994

Mr Rahul Divan
Company Accountant
Chang Fashions Ltd
142 Regent Court
London
WE4 1NN

Dear Mr Divan

Motor Police No ST9992342 on vehicle E 156 ESY

I wrote to you on 10 November concerning the renewal of the above policy and requesting a cheque for £526.00.

Since I have not received a reply the policy has now been cancelled and the vehicle is therefore no longer covered with this company.

Yours sincerely

R Massey

Robert Massey

Policies Manager

On checking it is found that:

(a)   A cheque for £526.00 payable to Star Line Insurance Ltd was issued on 17 November.

(b)   The cheque referred to in (a) above was debited to Chang Fashion Ltd's bank account on 24 November.

Using the headed paper on page 231, draft an appropriate letter to Robert Massey pointing out the facts concerning the cheque and requesting confirmation that the vehicle is covered under the Star Line policy. The letter, which is to be dated 2 December 1994, is to be signed by Rahul Divan.

Chang Fashions Ltd
142 Regent Court
London
WE4 1NN
Tel: 0181 803 6712

CENTRAL ASSESSMENT COMMUNICATION TASKS – COMART SUPPLIES LIMITED

these tasks are linked to the processing tasks which start on page 179

On 30 May 1995 a statement showing a balance of £25,320 was sent to Champion Computers Ltd together with a letter pointing out:

(a) Champion Computers Ltd's current credit limit is only £20,000.

(b) In view of the balance of the account, Comart Supplies Ltd are unable to fulfil an order received from Champion Computers Ltd for 6 Ensign 486 computers (total cost £4,250).

On 1 June the following letter was received:

Champion Computers Ltd
14 Seaview Trading Estate
Minehead
MN21 1SE
Tel: 01643 52586

31 May 1995

Ms Louise Ford
Company Accountant
Comart Supplies Ltd
22 Trull Road
Taunton
SO11 4NE

Dear Ms Ford

I refer to your letter of 30 May and the accompanying statement of our account. A cheque for £10,000 was sent to you by first class post on 1 May and this does not appear on the statement.

Although I appreciate that we have not been dealing with your company for very long, I am most concerned that you have not arranged for the delivery of the six Ensign 486 computers. These are required urgently to meet various orders received from customers.

An immediate response by return of post would be appreciated.

Yours sincerely

D Robinson

David Robinson
Accountant

You are asked by Louise Ford to investigate this matter. Your findings are listed as follows:

1   Cheque for £10,000 referred to in the letter - received on 3 May - credited in error to Chambers Computers instead of Champion Computers Ltd - you arrange for correcting entries to be made.

2   Before correcting the above error Chambers Computers had a balance of £32,326 and a credit limit of £40,000 - statement showing this balance sent out on 31 May.

3   Chambers Computers - owned by Christine Chambers - established business with whom Comart Supplies Ltd have been trading successfully for a number of years - Christine Chambers regarded as a valued customer.

4   Chambers Computers' account - often up to or slightly above the credit limit - in view of (3) above you agree with Louise Ford that it would be sensible to raise the credit limit to £45,000.

5   You are out of stock of Ensign 486 computers - earliest date manufacturer can deliver to you - 20 June.

6   In stock - Wallace 486 computers - similar specification to Ensign 486 computers - same price - could deliver immediately to Champion Computers Ltd.

TASK 1

Using the headed paper on the next page, draft a letter to David Robinson at Champion Computers Ltd. The letter (to be dated 1 June 1995) is to be signed by Louise Ford and should include the following:

(a)   An apology for the error (re the cheque).

(b)   Confirmation that the error has been corrected.

(c)   Details concerning the six computers ordered and the possibility of supplying an alternative machine.

(d)   A request for instructions concerning (c) above.

TASK 2

Using the blank headed paper on page 235 draft a letter to Christine Chambers of Chambers Computers (46 Northtown Estate, Taunton, Somerset, SO14 6PE). The letter is to be signed by Louise Ford and should include the following:

(a)   Details of the error (re the cheque) and its correction.

(b)   The balance of the corrected account and the current credit limit.

(c)   The decision to revise the credit limit.

Comart Supplies Ltd

22 Trull Road
Taunton
Somerset
SO11 4NE

Comart Supplies Ltd. Registered Office: 22 Trull Road, Taunton, Somerset, SO11 4NE.
Registered in England, number 2034586.

Comart Supplies Ltd

22 Trull Road
Taunton
Somerset
SO11 4NE

CENTRAL ASSESSMENT COMMUNICATION TASKS – SUMMIT GLAZING LIMITED

these tasks are linked to the processing tasks which start on page 192

TASK 1

On 18 November 1995 Summit Glazing purchased a consignment of patio doors from Vetro Ltd for £4,000 plus £686 VAT (Invoice no. D3472). The invoice offered a 2% cash discount for payment within 7 days. Summit Glazing paid the invoice by sending a cheque for £4,606 on 20 November. The cheque should have arrived within 7 days from the date of the invoice as it was sent by first class post. A statement dated 30 November showing a balance of £80 has now been received from Vetro Ltd.

Using the headed paper on the next page, draft a letter (dated 1 December 1995), to be signed by Mary Owen, explaining the situation and requesting that the appropriate action be taken. The letter will be faxed to Edward Frazer at Vetro Ltd, Unit 23 Gorse Industrial Estate, Manchester MN12 2BG.

TASK 2

During a review of overdue accounts in the sales ledger, Mary Owen notes that no payment has been received from Hayden Construction since June 1995, in spite of efforts made to recover the balance owing. Mary has heard from another creditor that the owner of Hayden Construction is now living in Australia. She feels that the debt should be written off, but the writing off of bad debts has to be sanctioned by Chris Cooper, the Managing Director. The file for Hayden Construction shows the following information:

Hayden Construction

Balance £530 (Goods supplied during February 1995)

Last payment received 8 June 1995

Recorded delivery sent 24 August 1995 - returned marked "premises unoccupied"

Debt collection agency report which stated that they were unable to trace the owner James Hayden

You are required to draft a suitable memorandum (datd 1 December 1995) to Chris Cooper informing him of the facts and seeking his authorisation to write off the Hayden Construction bad debt, using the stationery provided on page 238.

Summit Glazing Ltd
14-16 Ham Lane
Swindon
SW32 7FT
Tel: 01793 635542

MEMORANDUM

To:

From:

Date:

Subject:

CENTRAL ASSESSMENT COMMUNICATION TASKS – BLOOMERS LIMITED

these tasks are linked to the processing tasks which start on page 204

TASK 1

At present Bloomers Ltd's petty cash is kept in a fabric cash bag in an unlocked drawer. When the petty cash book is balanced and the petty cash is counted there is frequently a shortfall of cash for which there is no obvious explanation. As you are to be given responsibility for petty cash, Paul Lazenby has asked you to recommend measures which can be introduced to improve the security of the petty cash.

You are required to prepare a memo to Paul Lazenby detailing your recommendations, using the stationery provided below. The date is 1 June 1996.

MEMORANDUM

To:

From:

Date:

Subject:

BLOOMERS LIMITED – TASK 2

The bank statement received on 1 June showed that the Northern Bank plc had charged Bloomers Ltd £70 for its services. Bloomers Ltd's monthly bank charges do not normally exceed £50. Paul Lazenby is concerned about this significant increase in charges as there has not been any noticeable increase in banking transactions.

Using the headed paper shown below, you are required to prepare a letter (dated 1 June 1996) to the bank manager, David Williams, which is to be signed by Paul Lazenby. The bank's address is Northern Bank plc, 120 Lower High Street, York YK12 5SW. Your letter should express concern over the increase in charges and request an explanation. When drafting the letter you should bear in mind that Bloomers has a good relationship with its banker and has always been satisfied with the service provided.

Bloomers Ltd

12 Nightingale Arcade

York

YK12 3DC

Bloomers Ltd Registered Office: 12 Nightingale Arcade, York YK12 3DC

Registered in England, number 4643757

CENTRAL ASSESSMENT COMMUNICATION TASKS – MMS TEXTILES LIMITED

these tasks are linked to the processing tasks which start on page 215

The account of Window Box Ltd, a customer of MMS Textiles Ltd, is overdue for payment. A copy of the current Window Box Ltd statement of account, which was sent out on 31 October 1996, is given below. MMS Textiles gives its credit customers 30 days credit from the date of supply. This is clearly stated on all MMS Textiles' invoices.

STATEMENT OF ACCOUNT

MMS Textiles Ltd
Unit 34 Brooklands Estate
Walsall
WA3 7ZX

Tel: (01922) 211311
Fax: (01922) 231461
VAT Reg No. 465 765811

Window Box Ltd
12/13 Market Street
West Bromwich
WE2 24LK

Date	Reference	Debit £ p	Credit £ p	Balance £ p
1996 Oct 1	Balance brought forward			274 50
Oct 4	Invoice no. 19861	435 75		710 25
Oct 9	Invoice no. 20129	235 00		945 25
	Amount now due			945 25

Registered Office: Unit 34 Brooklands Est, Walsall WA3 7ZX
Registered Number 6516428

TASK 1

Using the letterhead on the next page, draft a letter (dated 1 December 1996) to James Sinclair at Window Box Ltd pointing out that their account is overdue and requesting immediate payment of the outstanding balance. A copy of the statement is to be enclosed with the letter.

MMS Textiles Ltd
Unit 34 Brooklands Estate
Walsall
WA3 7ZX
Tel: (01922) 211311 Fax: (01922) 231461

MMS Textiles Ltd. Registered Office: Unit 34 Brooklands Estate, Walsall WA3 7ZX

Registered in England, number 6516428

MMS TEXTILES LTD – TASK 2

Window Box Ltd is not to be supplied with any more goods on credit until their account is cleared. Using the form shown on page 84, prepare a memorandum (dated 1 December 1996) to Mohammed Saleem, Sales Manager, explaining the situation and stating that goods should not be supplied until you tell him that Window Box Ltd has cleared its existing debt.

appendix

This appendix of photocopiable material comprises the following documents and layouts:

DOUBLE-ENTRY ACCOUNTS

Dr | | | | | | Cr

Date	Details	Amount	Date	Details	Amount
		£			£

Dr | | | | | | Cr

Date	Details	Amount	Date	Details	Amount
		£			£

Dr | | | | | | Cr

Date	Details	Amount	Date	Details	Amount
		£			£

THE JOURNAL

Date	Details	Folio	Dr	Cr

Date	Details	Folio	Dr	Cr

Date	Details	Folio	Dr	Cr

	Sales Day Book					
Date	Customer	Invoice No	Folio	Gross	VAT	Net
				£ p	£ p	£ p

Sales Returns Day Book						
Date	Customer	Credit Note No	Folio	Gross	VAT	Net
				£　p	£　p	£　p

Analysed Sales Day Book

Date	Customer	Invoice no	Folio	Gross		VAT		Plants		Shrubs		Trees	
				£	p	£	p	£	p	£	p	£	p
1997													

Purchases Day Book						
Date	Supplier	Invoice No	Folio	Gross	VAT	Net
				£ p	£ p	£ p

	Purchases Returns Day Book					
Date	Supplier	Credit Note No	Folio	Gross	VAT	Net
				£ p	£ p	£ p

Analysed Purchases Day Book

Date	Supplier	Invoice no	Folio	Gross		VAT		Goods for resale		Printing		Telephone		Other expenses			
				£	p	£	p	£	p	£	p	£	p	£	p		
1997																	

CASH BOOK

Date	Details	Discount allowed £	VAT £	Cash £	Bank £

Date	Details	Discount received £	VAT £	Cash £	Bank £

ANALYSED CASH BOOK (RECEIPTS)

Date	Details	Foiio	Cash		Bank		Discount allowed		VAT		Sales		Sales ledger		Sundry	
			£	p	£	p	£	p	£	p	£	p	£	p	£	p

ANALYSED CASH BOOK (PAYMENTS)

Date	Details	Foiio	Cash £ p	Bank £ p	Discount received £ p	VAT £ p	Purchases £ p	Purchases ledger £ p	Sundry £ p

PETTY CASH BOOK

Receipts	Date	Details	Voucher No.	Payment	Analysis columns				
					VAT	Postages	Travel	Meals	Stationery
£ p				£ p	£ p	£ p	£ p	£ p	£ p

STATEMENT

to

date

date	details	debit £	credit £	balance £

AMOUNT NOW DUE	